THE ELEMENTS OF LOGIC

THE ELEMENTS OF LOGIC

For Use in Computer Science, Mathematics, and Philosophy

William J. Edgar

State University College of
Arts and Sciences

Geneseo, New York

PERGAMON

SCIENCE RESEARCH ASSOCIATES, INC.
Chicago, Henley-on-Thames, Sydney, Toronto
A Maxwell Pergamon Publishing Company

Acquisition Editor   Nancy Osman
Project Editor   Richard E. Myers
Production Administrator   Steve Leonardo
Text/Cover Designer   Kirk G. Panikis
Composition   Graphic Typesetting Service

Library of Congress Cataloging-in-Publication Data
Edgar, William J.
      The elements of logic : for use in computer science, mathematics,
   and philosophy / William J. Edgar.
         Includes index.
         ISBN 0-574-18755-3 :
         1. Logic. Modern.   2. Logic, Symbolic and mathematical.
      I. Title.
      BC38.E33 1988   88-23402
      160--dc19   CIP

Contents

Preface

"Where is the supplementary logic text to go with courses in computer science and discrete mathematics?" The author of that query, an editor who probably wishes to remain anonymous, had spotted a gap. When the question was posed, I had no reply. I do now. The text is contained in the following pages.

It is not uncommon for instructors in computer science and discrete mathematics to presume that students entering their courses have been grounded in the fundamentals of logic. In fact, most students entering such courses have not had a formal course in logic. Many of them were introduced to truth tables by their high school teachers, and some were also shown a few proofs in propositional logic. But most students know nothing of monadic predicate logic, general predicate logic, or higher-order logic. Hardly any undergraduate courses in mathematics and computer science require a logic course as a prerequisite. A few authors, such as those of certain discrete mathematics texts, have recognized this difficulty and devoted a short chapter or two to logical concepts. When such chapters are provided, they tend to be brief and incomplete. Some, for example, do not cover predicate logic. As a result, many students in computer science and mathematics face, in the parlance of deterrence, a logic gap.

Students facing this gap have little time in which to bridge it. They need a book that is short, inexpensive, easy to read, abundant in exercises (with answers), thorough, not too hard, and that covers all fundamental topics in deductive logic. Introductions to Aristotelian logic, informal fallacies, definition, the foundations of probability, the philosophy of science, the philosophy of logic, and other topics commonly appended to introductory logic texts can wait until another time. The book should also be suitable as the text for a three- to four-week component of a course.

The criteria of the last paragraph have shaped this book. This text differs from standard introductory logic texts in scope and level of difficulty. The difference in scope is outlined above. A scan of the exercises in this book will show that most of them are elementary. The purpose of the book is to provide students with a clear understanding of, say, what is required in a formal proof. Such understanding requires one to work through problem sets, but the problems need not be complex.

I began the first chapter with a version of Zeno's bisection paradox because the argument is valid, apparently sound, and thus extremely irritating. Those committed to finding out what is wrong with this argument are likely to be more receptive to the general problem of evaluating arguments. I also introduced all levels of logic in the first chapter, a deviation from the standard practice of introducing propositional logic, truth tables, proofs in propositional logic, and then turning to monadic predicate logic. I varied from standard practice for two reasons: (a) I wanted to show that logical form is all-important in deductive logic and that the level of detail in representing logical form separates the levels of logic. This is best shown by contrasting translations of statements into propositional logic, monadic predicate logic, and general predicate logic. (b) I wanted to introduce the translation problem as a unit, before turning to the evaluation of arguments. The translation problem, of course, is usually characterized as a problem of representation by those who work in the area of artificial intelligence.

Chapter 2 presents truth tables and their uses, with the exception of the task of determining the invalidity of an argument. This is covered in Chapter 3, Section 2. The inclusion of normal forms and logic gates at the end of Chapter 2 is largely informational. I do not expect students who are acquiring the fundamentals of logic in a short time to spend much time on either topic. Thus no exercises have been included for those sections.

The remainder of the book's organization is standard, with the exceptions of attention to certain psychological problems faced by those new to theorem proving and a brief look at the concepts of consistency and deductive completeness. Students are usually amazed to discover they can follow a thirty-step proof in class and have no idea where to begin a three-step proof at home. It is reassuring for them to learn that their problem is well-known and is based on the difference between recognizing a rule and knowing when to apply a rule to a particular situation. Consistency and completeness are addressed in the last section of the book, to let students know that people have tried to find a general answer to the question of what is computable and what is not.

I chose to summarize major definitions in a glossary rather than using the space-consuming device of setting these definitions off in special boxes throughout the text. In an effort to make the book read easily, I have been a bit casual in using single quotes to preserve the use-mention distinction. Single quotes have been used when introducing notation and when clarity would be lost if they were not used.

As indicated, the answer to every exercise has been provided at the end of the book. The only danger in this provision lies in the impatience of some students, which leads them to abandon the search after a few minutes. This danger does not outweigh the importance of offering a way for students to check their efforts.

I am indebted to Catherine Wagner of Cornell University for many suggestions which have improved the book. My thanks to Appie van de Liefvoort of the University of Missouri-Kansas City and Robert Simmons of the University of Texas at Austin for their critical comments on the text, and the patience and editorial skills of Richard Myers. Gwen Skrzeczkowski proofed the exercises and their answers. And I simply cannot permit Nancy Osman to remain anonymous. She asked the question which generated the book. How, then, could I neglect Stacey Edgar, the formal, efficient, and final cause of the circumstance in which the question occurred?

How to Read This Book

(1) Put a question mark next to any sentence you do not fully understand and continue to read.

(2) Do all of the exercises for each section as you proceed through the book. Check your answers only after you are pretty satisfied with your work. You will learn very little if you let the answers given in the back of the book "guide" you through the exercises. Have patience. If you get stuck on a problem, go on to the next one. On occasion wait a day or two before coming back to a problem which is causing you trouble. Sometimes your nervous system does amazing things while you sleep.

(3) Review the examples given in the book to see if they shed any light on the problems you face.

(4) Be careful when dealing with definitions and rules. A definition is a test or a set of tests. Exactly what is the test? A rule is an instruction or a set of instructions. Exactly what are these instructions? When you use a rule follow the instructions very carefully.

(5) As you proceed through the book, check back and see if you can erase some of those question marks. By the time you finish, you should be able to erase nearly all of them (perhaps every one).

(6) Logic problems come in nice little units, so you can fool with a few of them during a fifteen-minute break, take up something else, and then come back to them with virtually no preparation. So don't think you have to set large blocks of time aside to go through this book. The book is easy to read.

(7) The following is redundant, but I cannot stress it too much. There is no substitute for doing problems. One does not learn logic by memorizing some words; one acquires logical concepts by being able to use them to get certain jobs done. If you cannot do the exercises, you really don't understand the material.

(8) Initially, some exercises, especially proofs, are frustrating. You have to choose certain rules to solve a problem and the book doesn't provide a formula for choosing those rules. But then there is no formula for playing tennis. One gets better at tennis by playing. One gets better at logic by working on problems. To aid you, the exercises in this book have been ordered so that the easiest ones are first. Once you get going, you'll find that doing them is fun.

CHAPTER

1

Logical Form

With hindsight, I can say that the best thing for me to have done ten years ago would have been to take a course in logic. I have persuaded my students to do so, but never did so myself.

David Gries, *The Science of Programming* (1981)

Section 1

Why Worry about Logic?

In the neighborhood of 450 B.C., a Greek named Zeno presented humankind with an argument,which I shall paraphrase as follows:

Premise 1. Every interval of space contains an infinite number of locations.

Premise 2. If every interval of space contains an infinite number of locations, then if it is possible for you (fill in your name) to go to your refrigerator, you can go by, one at a time, all of the locations between you and your refrigerator. (I assume you're not reading this in your refrigerator.)

Premise 3. You cannot go by, one at a time, all of the locations between you and your refrigerator. (Some of them form an infinite sequence which is between you and your refrigerator door and you'd have to run through that sequence—which has no last term—before you got to the door. The sequence in question consists of the location halfway between you and the door, the location which is three-quarters of the way, the one which is seven-eighths, and so on ad infinitum. We're not adding up subintervals here. We're just counting, and there is no end to the things which must be counted before you get to the door.)

Therefore: It is not possible for you to go to your refrigerator.

Is this a good argument? Most of you will say that it is not and, perhaps, some of you will react by going to your refrigerator. In so doing, you will have rejected the conclusion of this argument. But I didn't ask you if the conclusion of the argument was any good, I asked you if the overall argument was any good. You may reply that any argument with a bad conclusion cannot be a good argument. In one sense you will be correct. In another sense you will not be correct. Exactly what is involved in evaluating an argument?

An *argument* consists of two of more statements where one of those statements is said to follow from the others. The statement which is said to follow from the others is called the *conclusion*, and the statements from which it follows are called the *premises*. There are three separate tasks to complete when evaluating an argument stated in an everyday language such as English. First, you must understand the statements in the argument. If you do not, there will be no way for you to determine whether the premises of the argument are true or false. For example, if the first premise of an argument was "All blurfs are slithey," you ought to demand a clarification of "blurf" and "slithey" before proceeding. Suppose you are asked whether the following claim is true or false: "The Löwenheim-Skolem theorem places an upper bound on multiplicity." Clearly, you must answer another question before trying to determine whether this claim is true: Do I understand what has been said? This prior question is important, but it is not the central concern of logic.

The second step in evaluating an argument is to determine if the premises of an argument are true. Suppose someone says she can prove that Santa Claus is a dog. Her proof contains two premises: (a) If three is an even number, then Santa Claus is a dog. (b) Three is an even number. (b) is false and so there is good reason to reject the argument. The problem of whether the premises of an argument are actually true belongs to the particular discipline in which reasoning is being used. One discovers the truth of premises about physical nature in physics, chemistry, and other natural sciences. One does not come to logic for these discoveries. Thus two of the three tasks required in the evaluation of arguments do not take place in logic.

The third task in evaluating an argument consists in checking the reasoning that takes one from the premises to the conclusion. Surprisingly, one can take on this task without knowing whether the premises make sense or whether they are actually true. We can ask, "If they did make sense and **if** they were true, would they force me to accept the conclusion?" The third task is what logic is all about.

I began this book with the Zeno argument because, although it is disturbing, there is nothing obviously wrong with the premises. This forces us to the third task in evaluating arguments, that of checking the reasoning. That is, we are forced to turn to *logic:* the search for methods of detecting good forms of reasoning, and the use of these methods to reject bad forms of reasoning.

Before pressing on with the task of checking the logic of the Zeno argument, a few words for those of you who harbor doubts about the premises of that argument. Premise 1 tells us something that mathematicians have held since 500 B.C., namely, that every interval contains, or consists of, an infinity of points. The alternatives to Premise 1 make a lot less sense. Certainly, no one would want to say that an interval contains no interior locations. If that were true, it would be impossible for anything to be anywhere in the interval. Something moving which hit the left-hand end of the interval would instantaneously be at the right-hand end. There would be no place, or location, for it to be in between. Intervals simply have interior locations. Well, why can't there be just a finite number; why must the number of locations be infinite? A finite number of locations would create the smallest subintervals, each of which had no interior points. And we just saw that the notion of an interval without interior points doesn't make much sense. Thus, Premise 1 looks like a true premise.

How about Premise 2? Well, if every interval contains an infinity of points, you will have to go by them as you pass through the interval. If you can think of a way around this, let me know. Premise 2 is true.

Is Premise 3 the false premise? If it is false, explain how you can finish running through, one at a time, a sequence of things which has no last term. You can't get to the end because there is no end. Of course there are locations in your refrigerator which are beyond this sequence. But your problem is that you can't get to these locations until you finish that never-ending sequence. Premise 3 also seems to be true.

Well, if the premises of the Zeno argument are true and the conclusion is false, the reasoning employed in going from the premises to the conclusion must be terrible. Just what is this reasoning? To answer this we must take a look at *the logical form of the argument*. We might begin by replacing the statements in the argument by letters, so that we can concentrate on the *logical operators* in the argument. We can see the logical structure of the argument even more easily if we replace 'not' and 'if, then' (the two operators in the Zeno argument) with simple symbols: '~' for 'not' and '→' for 'if, then.'

Let
I = Every interval of space contains an infinite number of locations.
R = It is possible for you (fill in your name) to go to your refrigerator.
G = You can go by, one at a time, all of the locations in the interval
    between you and your refrigerator.

The logical structure of the argument is now easy to see.

(1) I   [If this notation bothers you, start
(2) I→(R→G)   substituting the original English.
(3) ~G   You'll quickly discover that the notation
Therefore, ~R   is a great convenience.]

(2) says that if I is true, then R→G is true. (1) tells us that I is true. Thus, R→G is true. Now (3) tells us that G is not true. Well if R implies G, and if G

is not true, then R cannot be true. The reasoning here is flawless. The conclusion, ~R, that you cannot go to your refrigerator, has been logically demonstrated. There is nothing wrong with the logic.

If you still think there is something weird about the reasoning here, consider an argument with precisely the same form.

(1)' All even numbers are divisible by two.
(2)' If all even numbers are divisible by two, then if three is even, three is divisible by two.
(3)' Three is not divisible by two.

Therefore, three is not even.
More compactly

(1)' E
(2)' E→(T→D)
(3)' ~D

Therefore, ~T

Zeno's argument and the one about numbers are logically indistinguishable. They both fit the following logical form.

$$\frac{\rule{3cm}{0.4pt}}{\rule{3cm}{0.4pt}} \rightarrow (\_\,\_\,\_\,\_\,\_ \rightarrow \ldots\ldots\ldots)$$

~ . . . .
Therefore, –_ _ _ _ _

_____ is a slot, or a placeholder, into which any statement may fall. _ _ _ _ _ is a slot into which another statement may fall, and . . . . is a third slot. Instead of using these awkward spaces, or slots, let a lower case **p** stand for the first slot, **q** for the second, and **r** for the third. The *argument form* of the Zeno and the number arguments is

p
p→(q→r)
~r
Therefore, ~q

The **p** slot was filled by I in the Zeno argument and E in the number argument. The **q** slot was occupied by R and later by T. G and D fell into slot **r**.

Although we have shown only two examples of arguments that fit the argument form above, there is no end to the number of statements we can substitute in the **p, q,** and **r** slots. Thus there is no end to the number of arguments that can fit this form. If this form embodies correct reasoning, then any argument which fits this form will be a case of correct reasoning. Some of these arguments may have false premises. But **if** the premises were true, any rational person would have to accept the conclusion.

Exactly when does an argument have **good logical form**? It does when it is impossible for the premises of the argument to be true and for the conclusion to be false. How can we show when it is impossible for the premises to be true and the conclusion to be false? Read on; this book is an answer to that question.

Before we get down to business, five points of clarification will be useful. First, there are two kinds of arguments: **deductive** and **inductive**. This book is concerned only with the first kind. The book focuses on *valid deductive arguments*, that is, on arguments where it is impossible for the premises to be true while the conclusion is false. Inductive arguments deal in probabilities rather than impossibilities. An *inductive argument* is one where even if the premises are true and make the conclusion likely to be true, it is possible for the conclusion to be false. For example, given past performances (the basis for the premises of an inductive argument) it is highly likely that the world champion in tennis will beat Fred, who is an average player (the conclusion of this inductive argument). But the premises do not guarantee the conclusion, since the champion may suffer a crippling injury during the match and be forced to retire. A valid deductive argument guarantees the conclusion when the premises are true or taken to be true.

Second, there is a form of deductive reasoning known as **mathematical induction**. It is important not to confuse mathematical induction with the probabilistic reasoning characterized as induction in the preceding paragraph. To help keep the two straight, people often distinguish scientific induction from mathematical induction, where scientific induction is probabilistic reasoning and mathematical induction is as follows: Suppose in some universe you came across a line of flamingos that happened to be infinitely long. There is a first flamingo but for each flamingo thereafter there is yet another one in the line. You observe that the first flamingo is pink. A native of this universe who never lies then assures you that for any flamingo in the line: if it is pink, it is guaranteed that the flamingo that follows it will be pink. The principle of mathematical induction permits you to conclude, with certainty, that every flamingo in the line is pink. It cannot be any other way. You have seen that the first flamingo is pink. If the first one is, then so is the second (because that truth-telling native said that for any n, if the nth one is, then the n+1st one is). Thus, the second flamingo is pink, and if it is, then the third one is, and so on. Mathematical induction saves you the trouble of trying to do something you cannot do, namely, run through the whole sequence one case at a time. See Chapter 4, Section 2, for more on mathematical induction.

The third point of clarification is that the distinction between a concern with the logical structure of an argument and a concern with the truth of the premises of that argument is captured by the distinction between a *valid* argument and one which is *sound*. A *valid* argument is one where if the premises are true, the conclusion must be true. (We defined validity earlier as the impossibility of having true premises and a false conclusion. The two definitions are simply two ways of saying the same thing.) A *sound* argument is valid *and* its premises are, as a matter of fact, true. Since logicians are concerned with reasoning, they focus on the concept of validity. As noted earlier, determining the actual truth of the premises usually takes one into other disciplines, such as physics, biology, and psychology, where fact-finding is an important activity.

Fourth, I intend to use the terms "proposition" and "statement" interchangeably. I have avoided defining the concept represented by these terms because, although it is a very important concept, there has been a great deal of controversy surrounding its definition. This controversy will not bother us in this book, but I would be remiss if I ignored it altogether. One commonly encounters the following definition: "a proposition is a declarative sentence to which we can assign a truth value of either true or false, but not both." That is, a proposition is said to be a kind of sentence. One might object to this definition on the ground that a sentence, strictly speaking, is a string of notation that satisfies certain grammatical rules. Strictly speaking, sentences in themselves have no meaning. They are used to represent certain meanings. So, it is quite reasonable to say that two different sentences can express the same meaning. For example, "A valid argument cannot have true premises and a false conclusion" and "In a valid argument if the premises are true the conclusion must be true" are clearly different sentences. But they have exactly the same meaning, that is, they express the same proposition. There are two sentences here but only one proposition. Thus, one could claim, with good cause, that a proposition is *the meaning* of a declarative sentence. Why does this definition disturb some people? It is easy to see a sentence; it is not obvious that one can see a meaning. I'll not pursue this further. It is important to note, however, that propositions, or statements, are those things that can be true or false.

Finally, the Zeno argument is not typical of the arguments you will face. So don't let the puzzling character of the content of that argument lead you to believe that logic is a strange subject.

Before moving on to Section 2 make sure that you understand the following concepts:

- argument
- premise
- conclusion
- valid deductive argument
- sound deductive argument
- inductive argument
- the difference between scientific and mathematical induction
- the difference between a logical form and an instance of that form
- the differences among discovering the meaning of the premises of an argument, discovering whether the premises are true, and discovering whether the argument is valid

Section 2
Levels of Logical Analysis

The following statements have something in common, and it certainly is
not their content:

(1) "If Meg won, then Ed lost."
(2) "If some number is divisible by two, then some number is even."
(3) "If there is a Third World War, life on this planet may cease."

The first statement is about a contest, the second about numbers, and the
third about the possible consequences of nuclear war. Despite these differences, each statement begins with an 'if,' which is followed by a statement
(such as "Meg won"), which is followed by a 'then' (implicit in (3)), which
is followed by a second statement (such as "Ed lost"). Each statement has
the same structure, or form. That form is

(4) If _____ , then _ _ _ _ _ _ _.

If we adopt the notation used in Section 1, using **p** and **q** to represent the
blanks in (4), and '$\rightarrow$' to represent 'if, then' (4) becomes

(5) p$\rightarrow$q

   Now why would anyone want to ignore the content, or the meaning, of a
statement and focus on its logical structure? The answer is that the *logical
correctness* of an argument has everything do with the form of the statements in the argument, and nothing to do with their specific content. You
may not believe this answer right now, but you will by the time you finish
the book.
   If we aren't too interested in the content of a statement, we ought to save
ourselves the trouble of writing out all of the words which make it up.
Following the suggestions made in Section 1, we can let 'M' stand for "Meg
won" and 'E' stand for "Ed lost" in (1). Using our special symbol for 'if,
then,' (1) is now written 'M$\rightarrow$E'. Similarly, (2) can be written as 'D$\rightarrow$E'.
Note that 'D' here does not stand for a single term, such as 'divisible'; it
stands for the complete statement "Some number is divisible by two." This
economy of using a capital letter to represent a statement does not yield
logical forms. 'M$\rightarrow$E' is not a logical form. It is merely shorthand for "If
Meg won, then Ed lost." Note that 'M$\rightarrow$E,' 'D$\rightarrow$E,' and 'T$\rightarrow$P' are three different statements which have one logical form. That form, commonly called
implication, is p$\rightarrow$q. There are five basic logical forms but, before introducing the other four, it is important to step back and view what we are about
to do in a larger context.
   Consider another statement.

(6) "If all cats are quick, then some dogs are slow."

Although (6) obviously fits form p→q, someone who has an eye for detail might complain that p→q fails to capture the fine structure of (6). What fine structure? (6) is complex, containing two separate statements: "All cats are quick" and "Some dogs are slow." Each of these statements has an internal structure. The first claims a relation between all cats and quickness, the second between some dogs and slowness. The distinctions between all and some, between properties, such as being quick or slow, and individuals, such as certain cats and dogs, are ignored by p→q.

But isn't the internal structure of (6) simply the content of that statement, which we have agreed to ignore in our preoccupation with logical form? It is not. We could note that "All cats are quick" has the same form as "All A's are B," where we don't have a clue as to what A and B stand for. So even when we hit a more detailed level of analysis, we will be moving toward logical form.

We find, then, that there are two levels of structure in statements. The first consists of the structure that remains when one has decided to ignore the internal parts of simple statements. At this level, we see only simple statements and complexes of simple statements formed by the logical connectives (such as →) between those statements. Logic that does not penetrate further into the structure of statements is called *statement logic*, or *propositional logic*, or *sentential logic*. The analysis of expressions at this level will begin in Section 3 of this chapter.

When one presses for the structural details **within** a simple statement, one moves to another level of logic called *predicate logic*. In predicate logic we must find devices for representing terms like 'all' and 'some,' other devices for representing predicates such as 'being a cat' or 'being a thing which runs,' and devices for representing individuals such as Meg and Ed. Analyzing expressions at this level of detail will begin in Section 5 of this chapter.

Why would one run through logic twice, the first time ignoring the internal structure of statements, and the second time attending to these details? One answer to this question is that we can evaluate many arguments while remaining at the simpler level. And so we shall start with propositional logic and then move to more detailed analyses.

The major purpose of this section is to clearly distinguish propositional from predicate logic. Make sure you understand this distinction by turning to a friend who doesn't know much about logic and explaining in your own words what the difference is. As a check on your explanation, ask your friend what "levels of analysis" have to do with the difference.

Section 3

Representing Statements in English in Propositional Logic

Think of propositional logic as a world inhabited by three kinds of creatures: simple statements (each represented by a single capital letter), five logical connectives (each represented by a special symbol), and parentheses (for punctuation). The logical connectives will permit us to build complex statements from the simple ones. We already have seen the symbols for the logical connectives 'if,then' ($\rightarrow$) and 'not' ($\sim$). We also need a symbol for the logical connective 'and,' which is used when two statements are asserted jointly. For example, "Meg won and Ed lost." We'll use '$\land$' for 'and,' as in 'M$\land$E'. Someday we might have to deal with "Meg won or Ed lost." So we need a symbol for 'or'. We'll use '$\lor$' for 'or,' as in 'M$\lor$E'. It is common to include a symbol for 'if and only if,' namely, '$\leftrightarrow$'. We could omit 'if and only if,' as in "A if and only if B," because it is equivalent to "If A then B, and if B then A," i.e., (A$\rightarrow$B)$\land$(B$\rightarrow$A). Clearly, "A$\leftrightarrow$B" is more convenient.

So we have a big stock of capital letters, all the parentheses we need, and the following five logical connectives:

Symbol	Meaning	Example	Translation
$\sim$	not	"Fred did not know."	$\sim$F
$\land$	and	"Fred knew and Mary knew."	F$\land$M
$\lor$	or	"Fred knew or Mary knew."	F$\lor$M
$\rightarrow$	if, then	"If Fred knew, then Mary knew."	F$\rightarrow$M
$\leftrightarrow$	if and only if	"Fred knew if and only if Mary knew."	F$\leftrightarrow$M

We are now in a position to present the concept of *well-formed formula* in propositional logic. This concept is usually very carefully defined by what is called a **recursive definition**. A recursive definition is like mathematical induction in that it tells you the basic things that have the property in question and then it tells you the only ways you may build up complexes that have that property from these basic things. Logicians got sick of writing "well-formed formula," so they shortened it to "wff." Here is a recursive definition for the property of being a wff:

(1) The basic things: (A), (B), (C), . . . are wffs. (That is, every simple statement is a wff.)
(2) The complexes: If p is a wff, then $\sim$p is a wff. If p and q are wffs, then (p$\land$q), (p$\lor$q), (p$\rightarrow$q), and (p$\leftrightarrow$q) are wffs. (That is, only the five logical operators permit you to build bigger wffs from the ones you already have.)
(3) Nothing else can be a wff.

(1) above is called the **basis step** of our definition. (2) is called the **recursion step**. Note that since we have placed basic wffs in parentheses—such as (A)—every wff will be enclosed in parentheses. In this careful formulation, A∨B is not well-formed, but ((A)∨(B)) is. When we move back to our less formalized treatment of logic, we will use parentheses as needed for punctuation. When working informally we drop the parentheses around (A) because they are not needed to separate A from anything else. Similarly, if (A∨B) is the only wff on a line, we can drop the parentheses. In (A∨(B→C)), we can drop the outside parentheses, but not those on the inside. A∨(B→C) is unambiguous, but A∨B→C is not.

Note also that the second step, the recursion step in our recursive definition of being a wff, employed variables. This tells you that every wff is either simple, a negation, a conjunction, a disjunction, an implication, or an equivalence. Step 3 tells you, a bit redundantly, that there are no exceptions. For example, '→(B)' is not well-formed because it cannot possibly be generated by the procedures in the recursion step.

Our definition of being a wff permits us to formulate a definition of the **major connective of a wff**: If ~p is a wff then p is its **immediate component** and '~' is its **major connective**. If (p∧q), (p∨q), (p→q), and (p↔q) are wffs, then p and q are their immediate components and '∧,' '∨,' '→,' and '↔' are, respectively, their major connectives.

The fact that we have but five logical connectives means that there are basically only six kinds of statements in propositional logic. You will find it very important to recognize which of these six you face in a particular situation. In time, you will be introduced to rules of inference, each of which works on certain kinds of statements and not on other kinds. If you do not recognize the major connectives of the statements before you, you will not know which rules can be applied to those statements. Don't worry about these rules for now. For any given statement, be sure you can say which of the following six kinds it is:

Kinds of statements	Examples (in notation)
simple	A, B, C
negations	~A, ~(A∨B), ~((A→B)∨(C∧D))
conjunctions	A∧B, (A∨C)∧(D∨(E∨F)), (A→B)∧C
disjunctions	A∨B, A∨(B∧C), ~(A∧B)∨(~A∧~B)
implications	A→B, A→(C→D), (A∧F)→G
equivalences	A↔B, A↔(A→A), (A→B)↔(~A∨B)

Implication statements are also called **conditionals**. The first part of a conditional statement is called its **antecedent**. The second part is called its **consequent**. Equivalences are also called **biconditionals**.

So what are we going to do with all of this notation? Initially, we will translate statements in English into the notation of propositional logic. This is the first step in getting at the logical form of arguments. The illustrations

below are followed by a set of translations for you to do. Do them all.
Answers are in the back of the book.

Examples

Statement	Translation

(1) Two is even. — T
[Comment: Any other letter will do, such as E or A.]

(2) Ed is not wise and Ed is not well. — ~W∧~L
[You can't use W twice. "Wise" and "well" differ.]

(3) It's not true that Ed is wise and well. — ~(W∧L)
[The conjunction of Ed being wise and well is denied,
unlike (2) where each conjunct is denied separately. Note
that even if Ed is not both wise and well, he might be wise
(or he might be well). In (2) it is explicitly claimed that he is
neither. Thus (2) and (3) mean very different things.]

(4) If Ed dies, he'll miss class. — D→M
[Again, use any letters you like. Just make sure that each of
them stands for a complete statement.]

(5) Either Ed flies and he arrives on time,
or he walks and will not be on time. — (F∧T)∨(W∧~T)
[There are four statements about Ed here, even though his
name only appears once. "He walks" is really "Ed walks"
and "will not be on time" is an abbreviation for "Ed will
not be on time."]

(6) We cannot choose if and only if determinism is true. — ~C↔D

(7) We cannot choose only if determinism is true. — ~C→D

(8) We cannot choose, if determinism is true. — D→~C
[Note that "if and only if" is essentially a double implication.
'If' takes you one way (as in 8), 'only if' takes you the other
way (as in 7), and 'if and only if' takes you both ways (as in
7).]

(9) If Sue lies implies that Ed cries, then Liz will be angry at Sue. — (S→E)→L

(10) If Sue lies, then if Ed lies, Liz will be angry at Sue. — S→(E→L)
[Statements (9) and (10) do not mean the same thing. Thus,
it is important to use parentheses to show that they are different. If one wrote S→E→L, we could not tell whether (9)
or (10) is intended.]

(11) Ed lives in Darien or in Manhattan. — D∨M
[This example shows the meaning intended for the symbol
∨. That is, the ∨ in D∨M means "Either D or M, or perhaps
both." Ed might have a home in Darien, Connecticut, and
another one in Manhattan. When one intends 'either, or,
and perhaps both,' one intends *weak disjunction*.]

(12) Ed is alive or he is dead. $(A \lor D) \land \sim(A \land D)$
[This is an illustration of *strong disjunction,* where one
wishes to deny that both conditions can obtain at the same
time. Ed cannot be both alive and dead. We use no special
symbol for strong disjunction.]

Translate the Following into the Notation of Propositional Logic

Successful completion of the following exercises requires you to recognize
five things:

(a) The number of distinct statements in each expression
(b) The logical operators that connect these statements
(c) Whether a negation sign should be applied to an individual statement
   in the expression or whether it applies to a complex part of the expression [e.g., $\sim A \lor B$ vs. $\sim(A \lor B)$]
(d) When parentheses should be used to group together certain parts of
   the overall expression [As noted earlier,$(A \rightarrow B \rightarrow C)$ could mean either
   $(A \rightarrow (B \rightarrow C))$ or $((A \rightarrow B) \rightarrow C)$. These last two expressions are not
   equivalent. A careful reading of the original English should tell you
   which grouping is intended.]
(e) The major connective of a statement. If the statement is not simple,
   then is it primarily a negation, a conjunction, a disjunction, an implication, or an equivalence?

1. If May flies, Kay cries.
2. If May flies, then if Jay tries, Kay cries.
3. If May flies implies that Jay tries, then Kay cries.
4. May flies if and only if Kay cries.
5. May flies only if Kay cries.
6. May flies, if Kay cries.
7. Either May flies or Kay cries.
8. May flies and Kay cries.
9. May does not fly and Kay cries.
10. It is not true that both May flies and Kay cries.
11. Either May does not fly or Kay cries.
12. Neither May flies nor Kay cries.
13. Either May does not fly or Kay does not cry.
14. May does not fly and Kay does not cry.
15. If May flies and Ed tries, then Kay cries.
16. If Kay does not cry, then May does not fly.
17. If May flies then Ed tries, and if Ed tries then May flies.
18. Either May flies and Ed tries, or May does not fly and Ed does not try.
19. It is not the case that if May flies, Ed tries.
20. May is either in Chicago or on the Moon.

Section 4

Recognizing Logical Form in Propositional Logic

Suppose an extraterrestrial being gave you a machine which converted English into the notation of propositional logic. The output of this machine is always something like (A→B)∨(B→C), ~(A∨~B), ~A, or Z↔Q. These outputs are not logical forms. They are shorthand for particular propositions. However, each output has a logical form and in many cases the output fits more than one logical form. When you complete this section you should be able

(a) to identify the major connective of a statement (i.e., is it a negation, a conjunction, etc.?), and

(b) to identify all the forms, from a given list of forms, which the statement satisfies. When you finish this section you should also clearly understand the difference between a logical form and an instance of that form.

Examples	**Forms Satisfied**
(1) (A→B)∨(B→C)	p∨q, p∨(q→r), (p→q)∨r, (p→q)∨(r→s)

The basic form of this statement is p∨q. That is, the statement is a disjunction. It has two disjuncts, A→B and B→C. Since the disjuncts are complex, the statement also satisfies forms more complex than p→q. It fits p∨(q→r), with A→B falling into the p slot, B falling into the q slot, and C falling into the r slot. It also satisfies (p→q)∨r, with A into p, the first B into q, and B→C into r. It also satisfies (p→q)∨(r→s). You might balk at this claim because B is going to fall into two different slots, q and r. Different slots can be filled by the same letter, as is clearly seen by the following example.

(2) A→(A→A)	p→q, p→(q→r), p→(p→p)

(2) fits p→(q→r), with the first A going into p, the second into q, and the third into r. The basic form of the statement is implication (i.e., p→q), with A into p, and A→A into q.

(3) A→(B→C)	p→q, p→(q→r)

This statement fits the first two forms in (2), but it does not fit p→(p→p). The following is a very important point. Slots represented by the same lowercase letter must be filled in exactly the same way. (A∨B)→((A∨B)→(A∨B)) fits p→(p→p), but A→(A→B) does not.

(4) A∨B	p∨q

This fits p∨q and r∨s. These forms mean the same thing:

_____ ∨ _ _ _ _ _ _

A falls into the first slot, B into the second.

(5) ~A∨B   p∨q, ~p∨q

This statement is a disjunction. It fits p∨q, with ~A falling into p and B falling into q. It disturbs some people that a statement with a negation sign could fit a form which has no negation sign. But there really is no problem here. The form p∨q simply says, "Show me at least a disjuction; I don't care if the disjuncts are complex." So the form, not the example, controls this exercise. For example, ~p∨q says, "Show me a disjunction where the first disjunct is negated." ~A∨B fits this form, but A∨B does not. ~(A∨B) is not a disjunction; it is a negation. Thus, ~(A∨B) does not fit ~p∨q, but does fit ~p (with A∨B into p) and ~(p∨q).

(6) ~~(A∨B)   ~p, ~~p, ~~(p∨q)

~~(A∨B) really means ~(~(A∨B)), but it is common practice to omit the parenthesis following the first negation sign. Thus (6) fits ~p because the lead negation sign denies everything which follows. A∨B falls into the p slot in ~~p. (6) does not fit ~(p∨q) because ~(p∨q) says "Show me a statement the major connective of which is '~' and show me that what remains is a disjunction." But what remains after the lead "not" in (6) is a negation, not a disjunction.

Exercises

To make sure that you can recognize the basic form of a line and also recognize the other logical forms that a particular line satisfies, do all of the following exercises. Answers are in the back of the book. Since we need a form to cover simple propositions, I'll head the list of forms with p. Thus, A, B, C, etc., fit p. But since p is just a blank, or a slot, every expression fits it. The form p says in effect, "I am indifferent to whether the proposition has any structure or whether it is simple." The proposition must, of course, be well-formed.

For each of the propositions below, write the letter of each form of which that proposition is an instance. There is nothing special about the list of forms given here, other than that the list includes all of the basic forms.

Propositions	Forms
1. B→(B→B)	a. p
2. A→(B→C)	b. ~p
3. A∧(B→C)	c. p∧q
4. (A∧B)∨C	d. p∨q
5. ~((A∧B)∨C)	e. p→q
6. ~(A∧B)∨C	f. p↔q
7. A∧(B∨C)	g. ~p∨q
8. A	h. ~(p∨q)
9. ~~A	i. ~p∧~q
10. ~(~A∧B)	j. ~(p∧q)
11. ~(A∧B)	k. p∧~q
12. ~((A∨B)∧(C∨D))	l. ~p→q
13. ~((A∨B)∨(C∨D))	m. ~(p→q)
14. (A∧A)→B	n. p→p
15. ~~(A↔B)	o. p→(q→r)
16. ~(A→B)	p. p→(p→p)
17. A∨(A∧A)	q. ~~p
18. ~(A∧~A)	r. ~(p↔q)
19. ~~~A	s. ~(~p∨q)
20. ~(~~A∨~B)	t. ~(~p∧q)

Section 5

Translating English into the Notation of Predicate Logic

In Section 2 I noted that we could treat statements as elements, ignoring their internal structure, or we could attend to that internal structure. We are about to go inside. When we do, we will encounter parts of statements and these parts will not be statements. Consider three statements.

(a) Beau is a cat.
(b) Some cats are wild.
(c) All cats are animals.

In (a) the first thing we encounter is a proper name (Beau). "Beau" by itself is not a statement, but we will need a means of representing this name (and any other names we run across). We also encounter the predicate ". . . is a cat." A **predicate** is an expression which designates a property. We will need a way of representing predicates in our symbolizations. Proper names in this book will be represented by lower-case letters from **a** through **s** in our alphabet. Lower-case letters following **s (t–z)** will be used for variables. I realize that we used lower-case letters to represent logical forms when we were working in propositional logic. Trust me that no confusion will be introduced by what we are about to do. Predicates will be represented by capital letters. I know that we used capital letters in propositional logic to represent statements. Again, trust me. We will translate "Beau is a cat" as **Cb**, where the subscript **b** represents Beau and **C** tells us that he has the property of being a cat.

(b) above presents us with a slightly different situation than (a). We are not offered a proper name. In place of a name, we encounter the term 'some.' This term is commonly translated as 'there exists at least one thing.' Thus, "Some cats are wild" is understood to mean "There is at least one thing such that this thing is a cat and it is wild." We need a piece of notation to represent 'some,' or 'there is at least one thing.' We'll use $(\exists x)$ for 'some.' In "Some cats are wild," two properties are attributed to this something. Think of the **x** in $(\exists x)$ as the thing (i.e., 'there exists at least one thing' becomes 'there exists at least one x'). Letting 'Cx' stand for 'x is a cat' and 'Wx' stand for 'x is wild,' we can write "Some cats are wild" as

$(\exists x)(Cx \wedge Wx)$

$(\exists x)$ is called a quantifier because it provides information about the number of individuals being talked about, in this case at least one individual. We will see only two quantifiers in this book. $(\exists x)$ is usually called the *existential quantifier*.

"All cats are animals," (c), leads us to the other quantifier, the one for 'all.' We'll use $(\forall x)$ to represent 'all'. $(\forall x)$ is translated 'for each and every thing in the universe' or 'for each and every x,' where **x** means 'thing' or 'individual'. Let 'Cx' again stand for 'x is a cat' and 'Ax' stand for 'x is animal.' Then "All cats are animals" is represented as

$(\forall x)(Cx \rightarrow Ax)$

Why didn't we write $(\forall x)(Cx \wedge Ax)$? We did not because this last expression translates back into English as "Everything in the universe is a cat and an animal." This, of course, would include pop cans, footballs, and elephants. That is probably not what was intended. The device for avoiding this difficulty depends on the observation that **if** anything does turn out to be cat, **then** it will turn out to be an animal. That is just the way we translated "All cats are animals." $(\forall x)$ is known as the *universal quantifier*.

How do you know which quantifier to use in which situation? First, if you have a proper name, you don't need either quantifier. You don't have to say something as vague as 'there is at least one,' if you know who or what it is. You can name it. Second, when you read something in English, ask whether the author is referring to some individual or individuals, or whether the reference is to an entire class. Suppose, for example, you encountered, "Even numbers are divisible by two." The speaker hasn't used either 'some' or 'all'. But, pretty clearly, this is the kind of claim where 'all' is intended. Similarly, the author of "Children are present" probably does not intend that every child in the universe is present. In this case, 'some' has been dropped on the assumption that you'll fill it in. Obviously, if a speaker says 'all' or 'every' or another synonym, use **(∀x)**. If a speaker says 'some' or 'there is,' use **(∃x)**.

Parentheses are used to group together the predicate symbols which follow quantifiers. There is a very important reason for this use of parentheses. Let 'Cx' mean 'x is a cat.' If there is no quantifier in front of 'Cx,' then you don't know whether we're talking about one x, several x's, or all x's. Given this uncertainty, 'Cx' means '_____ has the property C.' That is, 'Cx' is an incomplete expression. Now suppose that someone wrote (∃x)Cx∧Dx. How is this to be understood? If no parentheses surround Cx∧Dx, then the quantifier, (∃x), applies **only** to the predicate symbol immediately to its right. This holds true for universally quantified expressions, such as (∀x)Ax→Bx. These expressions read as follows.

(∃x)Cx∧Dx: "Something has the property C and _____ has the property D."

(∀x)Ax→Bx: "If everything has the property A, then _____ has the property B."

Both expressions represent incomplete statements. This does not mean the expressions are not well-formed. Some wffs represent complete statements, others do not. Parentheses are used to show the *scope* of a quantifier, as they do in the following cases.

(∃x)(Cx∧Dx): "Something has properties C and D."

(∀x)(Ax→Bx): "If anything has A then it will also have B."

Generally, you can't do much with incomplete expressions. So, don't forget those parentheses when representing statements.

A recursive definition for being a wff in predicate logic is also available:

Basis step: (A), (B), (C), . . . , (Fa), (Fb), (Gc), . . . , (Fx), (Gx), (Hx), . . . are wffs.

Recursion Step: If p is a wff, then ~p is a wff.
If p and q are wffs, then (p∧q), (p∨q), (p→q), and (p↔q) are wffs.
If P is a wff and x is a variable, then (∃x)(P) and (∀x)(P) are wffs.

The fact that there can be wffs the quantifiers of which do not cover all of the predicates in the expression leads to a distinction between *free* and *bound* variables. First, the **x** we've been using is a variable. The term 'variable' is used in several ways. Since I will spend some time on different senses of 'variable' in Chapter 4, Section 2, and since the observations in that section are not needed here, I provide no definition here of 'variable.' Variables are attached to predicates, as in Cx. A variable is free if no quantifier applies to it. Thus there are no free variables in (∃x)(Cx∧Dx). There is one free variable (at D) in (∃x)Cx∧Dx, and the variables at C and D are both free in Cx∧Dx. A variable covered by a quantifier is bound (i.e., not free). The importance of the distinction between free and bound variables will become more clear as you move through Chapter 4.

I'll provide examples, with commentary, of translating English into predicate logic. You can check your understanding of this operation by doing all of the exercises at the end of the section.

Examples

Statement	**Translation**

(1) "Fullbacks are big and quick." $(\forall x)(Fx{\rightarrow}(Bx{\land}Qx))$
   [It is probable that we are talking about all fullbacks.]

(2) "Nietzsche was a sexist, but he wasn't sexy." $Sn{\land}{\sim}Yn$
   [We don't need a quantifier. This isn't someone or everyone, it is Nietzsche. So, the subscript **n** stands for Nietzsche. **S** is for 'sexist'. **Y** is for 'sexy,' which is not the same as being sexist. 'But' functions in the same way 'and' does.]

(3) "Some Martians are green." $(\exists x)(Mx{\land}Gx)$
   [Don't write $(\exists x)(Mx{\rightarrow}Gx)$, since that reads "There is something, and if it turns out to be a Martian then it will be green." The original statement was much more definite.]

(4) "All Martians are green." $(\forall x)(Mx{\rightarrow}Gx)$
   [Don't write $(\forall x)(Mx{\land}Gx)$, since that reads "Everything in the universe is a green Martian."]

(5) "Circles and squares are figures." $(\forall x)((Cx{\lor}Sx){\rightarrow}Fx)$
   [We translated the word "and" as "or". Why? Suppose you wrote $(\forall x)((Cx{\land}Sx){\rightarrow}Fx)$. That means, "If anything in the universe is both a circle and a square then it will be a figure." But nothing is both a circle and a square. Thus the English is a bit sloppy here, and you have to adjust.]

(6) "If Meg lost, then someone is sad." $Lm{\rightarrow}(\exists x)Sx$
   [We have a complex statement, one part of which involves a proper name, and the other part of which involves an existential quantifier. This raises no difficulty. Simply translate "Meg lost" as Lm, translate "Someone is sad" as $(\exists x)Sx$, and connect the two with $\rightarrow$.]

(7) "There are lions, tigers, and bears." $(\exists x)Lx{\land}(\exists x)Tx{\land}(\exists x)Bx$
   [Why three separate quantifiers? We could try $(\exists x)(Lx{\land}Tx{\land}Bx)$. That translates as "There is something (perhaps just one thing) which is a lion, a tiger, and a bear." In ordinary speech, people tend to take short cuts, in this case leaving out two "there exists."]

(8)   "No turtles are fast." $(\forall x)(Tx \rightarrow \sim Fx)$

(9)   "Not every turtle is fast." $\sim(\forall x)(Tx \rightarrow Fx)$
      [This translation is equivalent to $(\exists x)(Tx \wedge \sim Fx)$. There is
      at least one turtle which is not fast.]

(10) "Some turtles are not fast." $(\exists x)(Tx \wedge \sim Fx)$
      [Of course, this is equivalent to (9). Does "Some turtles
      are not fast" mean that some turtles are fast? That is,
      could one translate (10) as $(\exists x)(Tx \wedge Fx)$? No. It may be
      true that some turtles are not fast and it may also be true
      that none of them are.]

Special note: $(\forall x)\sim Fx$ means the same as $\sim(\exists x)Fx$. To say that nothing has
the property F is the same as saying that it is not true that there is something which has the property F. If one wishes to deny $(\forall x)\sim Fx$, one writes
$(\exists x)Fx$ (something does have F). Similarly, if one wishes to deny $(\forall x)Fx$, one
writes $(\exists x)\sim Fx$. $(\forall x)\sim Fx$ is not the denial of $(\forall x)Fx$. $(\forall x)\sim Fx$ says that nothing has F. $(\forall x)Fx$ says that everything has F. If you wish to deny any state-
ment, think of minimally what it would take to make the statement false. To
deny a universal statement, all you need is a single counterexample. However, when you deny the possibility of a counterexample, in effect, you
make a universal claim.

Translate the Following into the Notation of Predicate Logic

1. Some cats are blue.
2. Some cats are not blue.
3. No cats are blue.
4. Not all cats are blue.
5. All cats are blue.
6. It is not true that some cats are blue.
7. Some functions are continuous.
8. Wilma is bright.
9. Axioms are not derived.
10. Some statements cannot be proved.
11. If three is odd, some number is odd.
12. Every interval has a midpoint.
13. Some sequences don't end.
14. If Meg won, Ed lost.
15. If Meg won, someone lost.
16. Every number has a successor.
17. Zero is not a successor.
18. All triangles have three sides.
19. Some numbers are infinite.
20. Some spaces are non-Euclidean.

Section 6

General Predicate Logic, Orders of Logic, and the Principle of Identity

The predicate logic discussed so far has focused on individuals and properties. This level of logic, called *monadic* predicate logic, does not provide a way of representing relations among individuals. We cannot yet translate expressions such as "Sally is to the left of Rita" or "Some numbers are greater than others." The level of logic which provides for relations is called *general predicate logic*. Since relations are all-important to the study of mathematics, our interest in general predicate logic should be obvious.

Consider "Betty is to the left of Alice." We will use **b** for 'Betty,' **a** for 'Alice,' and **L** for the relation 'is to the left of.' This relation connects two things, and so **L** must have two subscripts. "Betty is to the left of Alice" is written

   Lba

   Note that the order of the subscripts makes a difference. If one writes "Lab," one claims that Alice is to the left of Betty.

   Consider "Some numbers are greater than others." If we spell out the content of this claim, we get "There exists at least one number and there exists at least one other number such that the first is greater than the second." We can represent this statement as

   $(\exists x)(\exists y)((Nx \wedge Ny) \wedge Gxy)$

   The multiple subscripts introduced by relations forces us to statements with multiple quantifiers.

   Consider "For every number there is a greater number." "For every" indicates that our translation must begin with a universal quantifier.

   $(\forall x)(\exists y)((Nx \wedge Ny) \rightarrow Gyx)$

Note again that the order of the terms in Gyx makes a difference. If one had written Gxy, the statement would read "Every number is greater than some number."

   Translation exercises for general predicate logic will appear in Section 7. The remaining question in this short section concerns what, if anything, lies beyond general predicate logic. Before approaching this question let us make sure the following claim is clear: **Monadic predicate logic contains propositional logic and general predicate logic contains monadic predicate logic.** The recursive definition of wff for monadic predicate logic is enough to show the inclusion of propositional logic in predicate logic. Of course, a similar definition of wff for general predicate logic includes the levels which precede it. An example may help to reinforce this point. Consider "Every number has a successor, and some number has no predecessor." We translate this statement into propositional logic as 'S∧P,' where S = Every number has a successor, and P = Some number has no predecessor.

S∧P can be represented in monadic predicate logic as

$(\forall x)(Nx \rightarrow Sx) \land (\exists x)(Nx \land \sim Px)$

where Nx = x is a number, Sx = x has a successor, and Px = x has a predecessor. Note that relational expressions (such as x is the successor of y) have been avoided in this translation. Also note that any statement in propositional logic can be represented in monadic predicate logic simply by representing the internal structure of each statement and preserving the logical connectives between statements.

How do we go from here to general predicate logic? General-predicate logic permits us to represent the logical structure of some statements in monadic predicate logic in greater detail, as a continuation of the analysis of "Every number has a successor, and some number has no predecessor" will show.

$(\forall x)(\exists y)((Nx \land Ny) \rightarrow Syx) \land (\exists x)(y)((Nx \land Ny) \rightarrow \sim Pyx)$

where Syx = y is the successor of x and Pyx = y is the predecessor of x. General predicate logic does contain the two simpler levels of logical analysis that precede it.

We now return to the question of whether there is anywhere to go after general predicate logic. At first sight, it would seem we have covered everything there is to talk about. We have, in general predicate logic, the capacity to talk about statements, individuals, properties, relations, and all the logical relations which connect statements, individuals, properties, and relations. There would seem to be nothing left, until we reveal one unwritten assumption: The quantifiers we use are assumed to range over individuals. This means that when one writes **(∀x)** one is saying 'for each and every individual thing' and when one writes **(∃x)** one is saying 'there is at least one individual thing.'

The understanding here is that an individual is not a class or a set or a collection of things. So we face a problem when we want to represent "Some sets of individuals are large." We cannot write

$(\exists x)(Sx \land Lx)$

because that says, "There is at least one individual such that the individual is a set of individuals which is large." An individual is not a set. Our problem is that we have not, thus far, presented a way to quantify over sets. Our quantifiers have been restricted to individual things. If we keep this restriction, we operate in *first-order general predicate logic*, i.e., GPL-1. If we remove the restriction, allowing us to quantify over sets of individuals, we move up to *second-order general predicate logic*, GPL-2. In GPL-2 we represent "Some sets of individuals are large" as (∃S)LS, where **(∃S)** stands for 'There exists at least one set S' and LS stands for 'S is large.'

It is obvious that we might want to quantify over sets of sets, such as the set of all pairs. To do so, we move to GPL-3. A moment's thought leads one to conclude there are an infinite number of levels in higher-order logic. For most "practical" purposes in mathematics, one need not go beyond GPL-2.

In fact, a great deal of mathematics can be done in GPL-1 by borrowing just one item from GPL-2. This item is known as *the Principle of Identity*. The Principle of Identity is simply the formal definition for two expressions referring to one thing. It is the definition of 'equals,' that is, '=.' Here it is:

$$(\forall x)(\forall y)((x=y) \leftrightarrow (\forall P)(Px \leftrightarrow Py))$$

In ordinary English, this says that x is identical to y if and only if x and y have all properties in common. For example, suppose you meet Liz, a woman who is five foot two, 118 pounds, black-haired, brown-eyed, twenty years old, born on November 17 in General Hospital in Port Charles (the only Port Charles) to a woman named Fredericka Brunhilde Matsumoto, at exactly 2:17 A.M. in Room 1030 (which was a single room). And suppose that a friend of yours describes a new acquaintance whose name is Mary, who is five foot two, 118 pounds, black-haired, . . . , which was a single. You are likely to conclude that Liz = Mary.

The Principle of Identity belongs to GPL-2 because it contains the quantifier (∀P), which reads 'For every property P.' A property may be viewed as a collection or a class. For example, one could say that the property of being red is the class of all red things and that the property of being triangular is the set of all triangles. Thus, to quantify over properties is to quantify over classes, and this is what is meant by the 2 in GPL-2.

With identity, one can talk about equalities and inequalities. GPL-1 with identity (borrowed from GPL-2) is the level of logic at which one can represent number theory. It is also the level at which some very interesting results occur about what is provable and what is unprovable in mathematics. These results, which take us beyond the current introduction, are sketched briefly in Chapter 4, Section 4.

Set theory, which involves quantification over sets, is sometimes referred to as a first-order theory. The preceding remarks suggest that it should be a second-order theory. This discrepancy can be explained by the decision to treat sets as units, just as the New York Giants might be viewed as one individual football team among many football teams.

Make sure you understand the following:

- The difference between propositional logic and monadic predicate logic
- The difference between monadic predicate logic and general predicate logic

- The differences between an individual, a property, and a relation
- That each level of logic captures those which precede it
- The difference between first- and second-order general predicate logic, i.e., the difference between GPL-1 and GPL-2
- The difference between quantifying over individuals and quantifying over predicates (or properties, sets, classes, collections)
- What sorts of things one could quantify over in GPL-4 (or in GPL-5, etc.)
- The Principle of Identity

Section 7

Translating English into the Notation of General Predicate Logic (First Order)

Since you are familiar with quantifiers, predicates, and relations, the only novelty in this section is complexity. The general problem of translating English into formal logic is complicated by the fact that the meaning of much that is said in English depends on the context in which the speech takes place. For example, "They are flying planes" might be uttered in the middle of a discussion about the activity of certain persons. One knows from the context provided by this discussion that "they" refers to certain people, and that "flying planes" means "controlling the planes." However, if this statement is presented without a context, one could take "they" to refer to the planes, and "flying" to present the status of the planes (that is, they are airborne and not grounded).

You will not, in this book, face a translation exercise as complex as the following one. It is included here to suggest that the problem of translating natural language, such as English, into a formal language, such as symbolic logic, is open-ended, very difficult and, as a whole, unsolved. Consider "Sense data are, in themselves, indistinguishable from the entities given in veridical perception." Sense data are those colors, shapes, and sounds which appear to you in dreams and when you are awake. Veridical perception is nonillusory perception, seeing it the way it is. This statement is clearly about a general relationship between sense data and the data provided in nonillusory perception. Thus the expression calls for universal quantifiers. The following translation might seem reasonable.

$$(\forall x)(\forall y)((Sx \wedge (Py \wedge \sim Iy)) \rightarrow Ixy)$$

If we retranslate this expression back into English and do it quite literally, we get "For any entity x and for any entity y, if x is a sense datum and y is a perception and y is not illusory, then x is indistinguishable from y." Ixy, which represents the relation of being indistinguishable, should not be confused with Iy, which represents the property of being illusory. Our translation has missed an important detail present in the original English: the expression "in themselves." The intent of this expression is to tell us that we must consider the sense data in question in isolation from everything else. When dreaming you suspect you are not awake because your best friend just turned into an aardvark. However, some of the colors you encounter in a dream are, in themselves, indistinguishable from colors one encounters in waking experience. How do we capture "in themselves"?

Trying to capture the intent of "in themselves" will involve introducing another quantifier for the person whose sense data these are, introducing terms which capture this person's ability to ignore the relations of the entity in question to everything else, and thus terms which capture "everything else." This is becoming messy to the point where we should drop the example and move on to manageable translations. Simply remember the reason for including this example.

Friendlier Examples	Translation
(1) Everyone loves someone.	$(\forall x)(\exists y)Lxy$
(2) Everyone loves everyone.	$(\forall x)(y)Lxy$
(3) Everyone loves himself (herself).	$(\forall x)Lxx$
(4) Someone loves everyone.	$(\exists x)(\forall y)Lxy$
(5) Someone loves someone.	$(\exists x)(\exists y)Lxy$
(6) New York is between Boston and Philadelphia.	Bnbp
(7) Someone loves Doris.	$(\exists x)Lxd$

Exercises (Answers appear on pages 120 to 121)

Translate each of the following into the notation of general predicate logic.

1. Zero is not the successor of any number.
2. There is no greatest number.
3. There is a least number (natural number).
4. Between every two points there is a third point.
5. If a father resembles his son, the son resembles the father.
6. No number is greater than itself.
7. Wilma sees all.
8. There is a dog not bitten by any dog.
9. Every dog bites itself.
10. Anyone who believes everything is a fool.
11. Anyone who believes nothing is a vegetable.
12. If x is greater than y and y is greater than z, then x is greater than z.
13. Causes precede their effects.
14. Sense data are not indistinguishable from bodies.

15. Kay never loses to Jay.
16. Kay never loses to anyone.
17. Some presidents don't consult with anyone.
18. Some books are better than others.
19. If two things are equal to a third, they are equal to one another.
20. There is a set that is the set of all sets that are not members of themselves.

2

Truth and Truth Tables

Nothing in the province of logic can be merely possible. Logic deals with every possibility and all possibilities are its facts.

Ludwig Wittgenstein, *Tractatus Logico-Philosophicus*, 2.0121

Section 1

The Concept of Truth and
the Law of the Excluded Middle

The aims of this book will not be served if we immerse ourselves in the philosophical controversies generated by attempts to provide a precise account of the nature of truth. With this in mind, I shall make four points about truth which are not patently mistaken and which will be adequate for this introduction. First, truth is a feature of propositions (statements, claims, assertions). If I claim there is a pen on my desk (and there is), my claim is true. The pen is not true, nor is the desk. They simply exist. They do not exist truly, nor could they exist falsely. Suppose I remove all pens from my desk and again claim there is a pen on my desk. My claim would be false. Being false would not be a characteristic of my desk, nor of the pens. We will talk about "attaching a truth value to a proposition." We will not talk about attaching truth values to other things, such as people, tables, or numbers. The number five is neither true nor false. "2+3=5" is true. "5+7=11" is false. These are propositions.

Second, true statements represent things as they are, false statements do not. The truth or falsehood of a statement depends on how things are, not on our beliefs, wishes, or desires. Thus, the truth of "There is life on Venus" depends on conditions on Venus. If there are living things on Venus then, whether I know this or not, the statement "There is life on Venus" is true. If there is no life on Venus, the statement is false.

Third, we can treat a statement as **if** it is true. We often do this in logic when we wish to discover the consequences of certain claims. We say, in effect, "Let's suppose these claims are true and discover what claims follow from them." We can also assume certain statements to be false and discover the consequences of these assumptions. Most of our work with truth in this book will be in the "as if it were true (or false)" mode.

Finally, it is commonly assumed when introducing logic that there are only two possible truth values: true and false. This assumption is often called the *Law of the Excluded Middle*: Every proposition has exactly one of two possible truth values. It is either true or false. In certain more advanced logic courses one encounters a topic called "many-valued logic," where "many" means "more than than two." One can run across three-valued logic, where the possibilities are "true," "indeterminate," and "false," or four-valued logic, where the possibilities are "necessarily true," "probably true," "improbably true," and "not possibly true." As you may have guessed, logic may have an infinite number of values. Whether all of these complications depend on two-valued logic is a matter of controversy.

There is also an intuitionist logic which omits the Law of the Excluded Middle. Intuitionists insist on constructive proof procedures, where if one is to show that something exists, he or she must produce it. With the Law of the Excluded Middle, one could argue that, say, a number satisfying certain conditions exists because the assumption it does not exist leads to a contradiction. At the end of this argument you still might not know which number satisfies those conditions. A constructive proof would require you to generate the number. Constructive proofs are extremely important in computer science. Nevertheless, in this introduction we will restrict ourselves to two-valued logic.

Section 2

Truth Tables and Possible Worlds

We have assumed that every statement is either true or false. It cannot be both and it cannot be neither. Keeping this simple observation in mind, and using "Mick Jagger lives" as an example, distinguish two questions: (1) What is the truth value of "Mick Jagger lives"? (2) What are the possible truth values of "Mick Jagger lives"? The first question is answered with a single value, either a true or a false. The second question is answered with two values, true and false. The question about possible truth values is often spoken of as a question about possible worlds (e.g., the world in which Mick Jagger is alive, and the world in which he is not).

"Mick Jagger lives" is a simple statement. Suppose we consider something just a bit more complex, such as "Mick is sick and Mick sings," and ask for the possible truth values of this claim. That is, how many possible worlds does it take to cover all cases in "Mick is sick and Mick sings"? Well, there is the world in which Mick is sick but sings anyway, another in which he is sick but refuses to sing, a third in which he isn't sick and does sing, and a fourth in which he isn't sick and doesn't sing. A complex statement made up of two simple statements generates four truth possibilities. A complex statement made of three simple statements generates eight truth possibilities, and a statement made up of n simple statements generates 2 raised to the nth power truth possibilities. A *truth table* is a device for displaying all of the truth possibilities for a given statement. Letting L = "Mick lives," C = "Mick is sick," and G = "Mick sings," the truth possibilities for L are listed below left and those for C∧G below right.

	L			C	G	C∧G
Possible world 1	T		Possible world 1	T	T	
Possible world 2	F		Possible world 2	T	F	
			Possible world 3	F	T	
			Possible world 4	F	F	

The truth table for C∧G above is obviously incomplete. It does not tell us how the conjunction C∧G turns out in each of the possible worlds. Recall that every statement has a single truth value. What is this value in possible world 1 for C∧G? The answer to this question depends on our definition of ∧ (and). An and-statement, a conjunction, is true when both its parts are true and it is false under any other conditions. So the completed truth table for C∧G is:

C	G	C∧G
T	T	T
T	F	F
F	T	F
F	F	F

For any two expressions p and q, the truth table for p∧q is given below. This is known as the truth table for conjunction.

p	q	p∧q
T	T	T
T	F	F
F	T	F
F	F	F

Since there are five basic logical connectives, there are five basic truth tables. These tables are the building blocks for all truth table calculations. The table for conjunction is given above. The tables for negation, disjunction, implication, and equivalence are given below.

Negation		Disjunction			Implication			Equivalence		
p	~p	p	q	p∨q	p	q	p→q	p	q	p↔q
T	F	T	T	T	T	T	T	T	T	T
F	T	T	F	T	T	F	F	T	F	F
		F	T	T	F	T	T	F	T	F
		F	F	F	F	F	T	F	F	T

The table for negation fits our ordinary intuitions pretty well. If some statement p is true, its negation is false, and if p is false then its negation is true. The table for disjunction is also intuitively correct. p∨q is true when *at least* one of its disjuncts (parts) is. The table for equivalence tells us that two statements are equivalent when their truth values match, as in lines 1 and 4, but not equivalent when the values do not match, as in lines 2 and 3. The table given earlier for conjuction also fits the ordinary view that a statement with a false part or parts cannot be wholly true.

The only table which would strike any thinking person as counter-intuitive is the one given for implication. The first two lines of that table pose no problem. If p and q are both true, then it is reasonable to count p→q as true, and if p is true and q false, it is reasonable to say that p→q is false. But what of lines 3 and 4? Why say that p→q is true, whenever the antecedent, p, is false?

Consider two implication statements: (a) "If Napoleon had won the battle of Waterloo, France would be an independent nation today." (b) "If Napoleon had won the battle of Waterloo, we'd all be speaking French." Since Napoleon did not win the battle of Waterloo, the antecedent of both (a) and (b) is factually false. The consequent of (a) is true and the consequent of (b) is false. Therefore, (a) fits the pattern of line 3 in the truth table for implication, and (b) fits the pattern for line 4. According to line 3 of the table, whenever the antecedent of an implication is false and the consequent is true, the entire statement counts as true. And whenever both antecedent and consequent are false, the entire statement is true (see line 4 of the table). It's tempting to say here that we don't know what to infer from false statements. Thus we might be tempted to put question marks in lines 3 and 4 under p→q. Obviously, logicians have not done this. Why not?

First, they would have violated the assumption of two-valued logic. There would now be three values: T, F, and ?. Second, they would face a non-truth-functional logic. A logic in which the basic truth tables are completely defined in terms of truth and falsehood is called a *truth-functional logic*. Truth-functional logics are powerful and it is relatively easy to obtain results about the overall characteristics of such logics. In a truth-functional logic, one does not run into situations where calculations terminate with question marks. In a peculiar sense of "practical," non-truth-functional logics turn out to be impractical, i.e., not terribly useful. The upshot of this is that logicians are committed to complete definitions in terms of trues and falses for each of the five basic tables.

But why must lines 3 and 4 in the implication table have to calculate to true? Compare "If Meg wins, Dave loses" with "Either Meg does not win, or Dave loses." If Meg does not win the second statement will be true. That is, there is an intuitive equivalence between p→q and ~p∨q. The truth table for ~p∨q is identical to the one supplied for p→q.

Thus far, you have been provided with five fundamental truth tables. These tables may be used to construct truth tables for more complex expressions. Suppose, for example, someone asks you to write out the truth table for (A→B)↔(~A∨B). How do you do this?

(1) Write to the left of the expression in question the possible truth conditions for the expression. Set up the possible worlds.

(2) If any simple statements are negated, calculate the result of the negation under the negation sign. You do this by looking at the truth conditions listed under the letter in the possible worlds set up. For example, in the illustration below, you find T,T,F,F listed under A. F,F,T,T goes under ~A.

(3) Next, calculate the truth values for expressions within parentheses. To do this, look at the logical connective in the expression, e.g., the logical connective in the first set of parentheses in the illustration below is →. Then use the basic implication truth table to get a column of truth values under (A→B). Do the same for the second set of parentheses. Note that here you have the results under ~A, the values under B (from the truth conditions to the left), and the "operation" of disjunction.

(4) So now you have calculated the result for (A→B) and the result for (~A∨B). Use those results and the truth table for equivalence to finish off the table. Your final result is the set of truth values under the ↔ sign. Your calculation should look like the following. I've spread the expression out so the columns are easier to see.

A	B	(A → B)	↔	(~A ∨ B)
T	T	T T T	T	F T T
T	F	T F F	T	F F F
F	T	F T T	T	T T T
F	F	F T F	T	T T F
(1)		(3)	(4)	(2) (3)

These instructions generalize to constructing any truth table. Start with the simplest calculations. Then move to the complexes made of those simple things. Then move to the expressions made of those complexes, and so on. Recall the recursive definition for wff given in the last chapter. One begins with simple wffs and then generates successively more complex expressions. Do your calculations in the same order, from the bottom up.

Even after the explanation just given, some students have been confused by step (3). They had forgotten that five basic truth tables were given (for negation, conjunction, etc.) and that one had to use these tables in constructing the table. Somehow they thought that everything needed for the calculation appeared in the table. Of course, this isn't true. You have to bring the five basic tables with you and use them to construct the table.

I'll provide a few more examples of truth-table construction, with much less commentary. I'll then turn to the question of how to construct a table when more than two kinds of statements (letters) are involved in the expression. Rather than providing exercises in truth-table construction, I'll move on to the uses for truth tables. You will have ample opportunity to construct tables in the context of having jobs for them to do.

Consider the truth table for (A→B)∧(B→A). I chose this particular table because of its second part, (B→A), the calculation of which has confused a few people.

A	B	(A → B)	∧	(B → A)
T	T	T	T	T
T	F	F	F	T
F	T	T	F	F
F	F	T	T	T

Note that I decided not to write the truth values for A and B under those letters in the expression being evaluated. It is tedious to do so, and you can just look to left (to the truth conditions) to see what they are. How did I arrive at the column for B→A? I read the truth conditions from right to left because, in B→A, B comes first. Thus line 2 turned out true, since it is the result of false implies true, and line 3 turns out false, since it is the result of true implies false. You might note that the final result for this expression, T,F,F,T, is identical to the table for p↔q. This tells you that p↔q is another way of expressing (p→q)∧(q→p).

Note that every truth table calculation has a single column which is *the* table for the expression in question. In the case above, the table is the column under the '∧' sign. All of those other T's and F's were merely aids in calculating the final result.

Don't be flustered by negation signs outside of complex expressions. Simply work from inside to outside. Get a column of truth values for an expression in parentheses and use the negation sign to flip them to opposite values. For example:

A	B	~(~(A ∨ B)	→	(A ∨ B))
T	T	F F T	T	T
T	F	F F T	T	T
F	T	F F T	T	T
F	F	T T F	F	F

The two columns under the interior parentheses are the same and result from using the truth table for disjunction. The left of these two columns is negated, yielding F,F,F,T (the result for the expression inside the outer parentheses that occurs before the → sign). The column under → is the result for the entire expression inside the outer parentheses. The truth table for the expression occurs under the leftmost negation sign. It comes from switching the truth values which occur under →.

What does one do when confronted with an expression containing three, four, or five simple statements? First, determine how many possible worlds are generated by the expression—how many rows will be in the truth table. As noted before, just count the number of different simple statements in the expression (the number of different letters), and raise 2 to this power. If there are two statements, for example, there are four rows in the truth table. Three statements (letters) yield an eight-row truth table, four letters require sixteen rows, and so on. The remaining problem is that of making sure we don't miss any possible truth combinations when constructing the table.

Suppose you are confronted with constructing a table for A→(B→C). You know there will be eight rows. These rows are supposed to capture every combination of true and false for three different statements. They must include the world in which all three statements are true, the one in which they are all false, and every combination in between. There is a simple device to guarantee that you won't miss any combinations, no matter how many possible worlds are involved. I'll use A→(B→C) to illustrate this device. Begin under the letter farthest to the right, C in this case, and alternate T and F for eight rows. (Recall that three simple statements generate an eight-row table.) Then move over to the B column. Now double alternate, first two T's, then two F's, for eight rows. Then move over to A, begin with four T's and then go on with four F's. If you had a sixteen-row table, you would begin on the right by alternating T and F for sixteen rows. Move left to the next letter and double alternate T's and F's for sixteen rows. Then move left again and alternate every four times. Finally, go to the letter farthest to the left and alternate every eight times. All of this does no more than set up the truth conditions to the left of the expression you are going to evaluate.

I haven't taken up space with these more complex truth tables, since large truth tables are suitable for computers but not for human beings. A typical argument might require a truth table of one hundred twenty-eight or two hundred fifty-six rows. We are fortunate in having methods which liberate us from such calculations. Why then bother with truth tables at all? First, they provide the justification for the rules of inference we will use when constructing proofs. Second, the basic tables define precisely our fundamental logical concepts, such as negation, disjunction, and implication. Third, we will need the basic tables in truth-table reasoning, the reasoning which short-cuts those lengthy calculations. Thus exercises involving truth tables will be relatively simple.

Three tasks involving truth tables will concern us. In Section 3, we will use truth tables to determine whether a given statement is a tautology, a contingency, or a contradiction. In Section 4, truth tables will be used to determine whether or not two statements are logically equivalent. In Chapter 3, Section 2, we will show that truth tables can be used to determine whether an argument is valid or invalid.

Section 3

Tautologies, Contingencies, and Contradictions

A *tautology* is a statement with a truth table which calculates to true on every line. A tautology is true in all possible worlds.

A *contingency* is a statement with a truth table which contains at least one true and at least one false. A contingency is true in at least one possible world and false in at least one other world.

A *contradiction* is a statement with a truth table which calculates to false on every line. A contradiction is false in every possible world.

We will find it useful to be able to make the distinctions above, especially when we concern ourselves with rules of inference that are supposed to work in every possible world. The illustrations below are followed by a set of exercises where you are to determine, by using truth tables, whether the statements in question are tautologies, contingencies, or contradictions.

(1) A→(B→A) is a tautology, as the table below shows.

A	B	A	→	(B → A)
T	T	T	T	T
T	F	T	T	T
F	T	F	T	F
F	F	F	T	T

The column under the first → sign is the truth table for this expression. This column contains nothing but T's.

(2) ~(A∨B)→(A∨B) is contingent.

A	B	~(A ∨ B)		→	(A ∨ B)
T	T	F	T	T	T
T	F	F	T	T	T
F	T	F	T	T	T
F	F	T	F	F	F

The last line generates an F under the → sign, because ~(A∨B) calculates to true and A∨B caculates to false on the same line. As you recall, "true implies false is false."

(3) (A→B)∧(A∧~B) is a contradiction.

A	B	(A → B)	∧	(A ∧ ~B)
T	T	T	F	T F F
T	F	F	F	T T T
F	T	T	F	F F F
F	F	T	F	F F T

The column under the first ∧ sign is the truth table for this expression and it contains nothing but F's.

(4) The simple expression D is contingent. Some people have trouble constructing the truth table for an expression like D because by now they are so used to four-line truth tables that they try to construct one for D. D, of course, has only a two-line table. There are only two possible worlds for D. It is either true or false. D's truth table contains one T and one F.

Exercises

Use truth tables to determine for each of the following whether it is a tautology, a contingency, or a contradiction. Answers to all problems are in the back of the book.

1. B
2. A∨B
3. A→(A→A)
4. ~(A∨~A)
5. ~(A∧~A)
6. B→B
7. (A→B)→(A→(A∧B))
8. A→(A∨Z)
9. ((A→B)∧~A)→~B
10. ((A∨B)∧~A)→B
11. ((A→B)∧B)→A
12. ((A→B)∧~B)→~A
13. (A→~A)∧(~A→A)
14. ~((A∧B)∨(~A∧~B))
15. (A∧B)→A
16. A→(A∧B)
17. (A∨Z)→A
18. ((A∨B)∧~B)→~A
19. ~(A→A)
20. ((A→B)∧(B→C))→(A→C)

Section 4

Logical Equivalences

Some logical expressions can have different form. They simply don't look alike, and yet they have the same meaning. Consider the difference between "Either Ed eats or Ed drinks" and "Either Ed drinks or Ed eats." The first expression can be translated as E∨D and second as D∨E. These two expressions obviously do not have the same form, but just as obviously they mean exactly the same thing. How does one determine in general when expressions with different logical forms have the same meaning? The answer to this is that whenever two expressions have the same truth table they are *logically equivalent*. We test for the condition of logical equivalence with a truth table, as follows.

(a) Write down the expressions in question with an equivalence sign between them.
(b) Write the truth table for this equivalence.
(c) If the truth table is a tautology, the expressions are equivalent, and if it is not, the expressions are not equivalent.

(1) Is A→B logically equivalent to ~A∨B?

A	B	(A → B)	↔	(~A ∨ B)
T	T	T	T	F T T
T	F	F	T	F F F
F	T	T	T	T T T
F	F	T	T	T T F

Since there are nothing but T's under the ↔ sign, this expression is a tautology. Thus, A→B is logically equivalent to ~A∨B. Note that the truth table for A→B is identical to the truth table for ~A∨B.

(2) Is ~(A∧B) logically equivalent to ~A∧~B? Some people think it is because it looks as though the negation ought to "distribute through the expression within the parentheses." Let's check it out:

A	B	~(A ∧ B)	↔	(~A ∧ ~B)
T	T	F T	T	F F F
T	F	T F	F	F F T
F	T	T F	F	T F F
F	F	T F	T	T T T

In lines 2 and 3 ~(A∧B) calculates to true while ~A∧~B calculates to false. Thus in possible worlds 2 and 3 one expression will be true at the same time the other is false. The expressions cannot possibly be equivalent.

De Morgan's Laws capture the correct equivalences between conjunctions and disjunctions. They are as follows:

~(p∨q)↔(~p∧~q)
~(p∧q)↔(~p∨~q)

Another important equivalence is *double negation:*

p↔~~p

Whenever in doubt as to whether two expressions are logically equivalent, simply run a truth-table test. Assure yourself that you can run such tests by doing the following set of problems. You can check your work by going to the back of the book.

Exercises

For each of the following, is the expression to the left of the ↔ sign logically equivalent to the expression to the right of that sign? That is, do the expressions have identical truth tables? That is, is the equivalence a tautology? A yes or a no will do for an answer.

1. A↔(A∨A)
2. A↔B
3. A↔(A∨B)
4. (A∨B)↔(B∨A)
5. (A→B)↔(B→A)
6. ~(A∨B)↔(~A∨~B)
7. ~(A∨B)↔(~A∧~B)
8. A↔~~A
9. A↔~A
10. (A→B)↔(~B→~A)

11. (A↔B)↔((A→B)∧(B→A))
12. (A↔B)↔((A∧B)∨(~A∧~B))
13. (A→B)↔~(A∧~B)
14. (A→B)↔(A→(A∧B))
15. (A→B)↔(A↔B)
16. ~(A∧B)↔(~A∨~B)
17. ~(~A∨C)↔(~~A∨C)
18. (A∨B)↔(~A→B)
19. (A∨(B∨C))↔((A∨B)∨C)
20. (A∨(B∧C))↔((A∨B)∧(A∨C))

Section 5

Disjunctive and Conjunctive Normal Forms

The material covered in this section and in the next is not essential for an understanding of the remainder of the book. I have included these sections to show that a certain kind of simplicity is available in logic, a simplicity which is of importance in computer design. If you are pressed for time, you might skip these sections and move to Chapter 3, Section 1.

In example (1) of the preceding section, it was shown that A→B is logically equivalent to ~A∨B. Since these expressions are equivalent, there would be no harm in replacing one of them with the other. Thus, every time we encountered A→B we could write ~A∨B. In fact, we could drop expressions of the form p→q altogether, and always use ~p∨q instead. In doing this, we would have eliminated a need for the symbol →.

If you did Exercise 11 of the preceding set, you proved that A↔B is logically equivalent to (A→B)∧(B→A). Since we just noticed a way to replace expressions of the form p→q with the form ~p∨q, we have a way to eliminate a need for the symbol ↔. Every time we would have written p↔q, we write instead (~p∨q)∧(~q∨p). We now have a logic where we need only three basic logical operators: ~ (not), ∧ (and), ∨ (or). We have lost nothing of importance in this reduction. We can express everything we could when we had five operators.

In one sense, moving to three operators is a move toward simplicity. Clearly, it would be easier to construct a machine which performed logical operations with fewer *kinds* of basic components. In another sense, the move to three operators makes things less simple. Which is easier to read, "A↔B," or its three-operator equivalent, "(~A∨B)∧(~B∨A)"? In any event, the move to fewer operators is available to us.

At a certain stage of logic, one steps outside of the operations within a logical system and asks the question of what in general can be proved in the system and what in general cannot be proved. One asks questions about the system as a whole and not just about a particular problem which arises within the system. Considering the system as a whole is really considering *every* expression which could possibly arise in the system. Such an examination would be simplified considerably if we could find a common form for all expressions. Two such common forms are called *disjunctive normal form* and *conjunctive normal form*. Every statement in propositional logic can be put into each of these forms.

A statement is in *disjunctive normal form* (DNF) if it is

(a) a simple statement or its negation; or
(b) a conjunction, the conjuncts of which are simple or are the negations of simple statements; or
(c) a disjunction, the disjuncts of which are simple or the negations of simple statements; or
(d) a disjunction, the disjuncts of which are conjunctions, where each conjunct is either simple or the negation of a simple statement.

Thus A, B, and C are in DNF; they fit condition (a). C∧D, ~A∧B, and ~B∧~D are in DNF, since they fit condition (b). ~A∨C, A∨(B∨C), and (A∨B)∨(C∨~D) are all illustrations of (c). (A∧B)∨(C∧D) and (~B∧C)∨(D∧~C)∨(A∧B) are cases of (d). The following are not cases of DNF:

(A∨B)∧(B∨C)   This is basically a conjunction, not a disjunction. In case (b) above we have conjunctions. Why are they in DNF when the expression to the left is not? We want to be able to say that every expression has a DNF. We permitted A alone in (a) above to be in DNF by viewing it as a "degenerate" case of a disjunction, i.e., a disjunction with only one disjunct. Similarly, we can view A∧B or C∧~D as degenerate cases of disjunction, where the conjunction is the single disjunct. Once these exceptions are put aside, every statement in DNF is primarily a set of or-statements.

~(A∧B)∨(C∧D)   This statement is not in DNF because negation signs in expressions in DNF can apply only to simple statements. Obviously, ~(A∧B) violates this condition.

(A∨B)∨(A→C)   This statement violates DNF because of the use of →. At most, three kinds of symbols are permitted in expressions in DNF: ~, ∧, and ∨.

How does one find the DNF of a given expression? The answer to this question involves certain rules which will be introduced in Chapter 3. The answer is complicated by the fact that an expression can have more than one DNF. Consider, for example, A→(A∧B). We can write this expression as ~A∨(B∧C) by using the equivalence of p→q and ~p∨q. ~A∨(B∧C) is in DNF. But (~A∧~A)∨(B∧C) is also in DNF and it is equivalent to A→(B∧C). (If you aren't sure of this, you can run the equivalence test outlined in Section 4 of this chapter.) There are many logical equivalences and, once one is familiar with these, it is possible to generate many expressions in DNF that are all equivalent to the expression in question. Since you are not yet accustomed to using these equivalences, I haven't really answered the question of how, in general, one can find the DNF for any given expression.

There is a special kind of disjunctive normal form, called *Boolean disjunctive normal form* (BDNF), which is easy to find once one has been introduced to truth tables. And since you have been introduced to truth tables, here is the method for finding the BDNF of any expression. This method is an example of an *effective procedure,* that is, a procedure guaranteed to produce the desired result (in this case the BDNF of any wff) in a finite number of steps. Here is the method:

(1) Write the truth table for the expression.
(2) Find the lines in which the expression calculates to true.
(3) Determine the truth conditions for these lines. Simply look and see what they are.
(4) Use these truth conditions to construct the disjuncts for the DNF of the expression. This step is illustrated in the example below.
(5) Connect the disjuncts with ∨ signs.

Let us find the BDNF of A→(A∧B):

A	B	A	→	(A ∧ B)		
T	T	T	T	T	A∧B	The line is true, as are A and B.
T	F	T	F	F		
F	T	F	T	F	~A∧B	A is not true, but B is.
F	F	F	T	F	~A∧~B	Neither A or B is true.

Since lines 1, 3, and 4 calculate to true, look at the truth conditions (at the left) for those lines. If you encounter a T, use the letter, such as A in line 1, as a conjunct. If you encounter an F, as you do under A in line 3, use ~A as a conjunct. Thus, the three true lines have generated the three parts of the disjunction for the BDNF of the expression. The BDNF for A→(A∧B) is

(A∧B)∨(~A∧B)∨(~A∧~B).

Note that the BDNF of our expression provides us with each of the sets of conditions under which A→(A∧B) turns out true. It is true when A and B are both true or true when A is not true but B is or true when neither is true.

Given the instructions just outlined how, can we find the BDNF of a contradiction? Step (2) tells us to find the lines in the truth table which calculate to true. In a contradiction, no lines calculate to true. It follows that contradictions do not have a BDNF. They have a DNF, as illustrated by A∧~A, which is in DNF.

Every expression also has a *conjunctive normal form* (CNF). The definition for CNF is very much like the one for DNF. Simply substitute conjunction for disjunction and proceed.

A statement is in CNF if it is

(a) a simple statement or its negation; or
(b) a disjunction with simple disjuncts or the negations of simple disjuncts; or
(c) a conjunction with simple conjuncts or the negations of simple conjuncts; or
(d) a conjunction, the conjuncts of which are disjunctions, where each disjunct of the disjunction is simple or the negation of a simple statement.

Statements such as A, B, and C are in CNF. They are also in DNF. Thus, some statements satisfy both CNF and DNF. Statements such as A∨B and ~A∨~C are viewed as one-conjunct conjunctions and, thus, are in CNF. C∧D and ~A∧~B are in CNF. (A∨B∨~A)∧D and (B∨C)∧(~B∨C)∧(B∨~C) are in CNF. The following statements are not in CNF:

(A∨B)∧~(A∨C)	Negations of complex statements are prohibited.
(A→B)∧(C∨D)	Only ~, ∧, and ∨ are permittted.
(A∧B)∨(B∧C)	The major connective has to be 'and' not 'or.'

We now turn to the question of how to find the CNF of a given expression. As with the DNF case, for each statement there are a variety of equivalent statements in CNF. Again, since you are not yet practiced in deriving logical equivalences (this will be covered in Chapter 3, Section 3), we turn to the truth-table method for finding the *Boolean conjunctive normal form* of a statement (BCNF):

(1) Construct the truth table for the expression in question.
(2) Note the lines in this table which calculate to false.
(3) Note the truth conditions for these lines.
(4) If the truth condition for a particular letter on the line is false, write

the negation of that letter as a conjunct. If the condition is true, simply write the letter as a conjunct.

(5) Negate each of the conjunctions generated by step (4).

(6) Use De Morgan's Laws and Double Negation to convert each conjunction into a disjunction.

(7) Conjoin all of the disjunctions resulting from step (6).

Let us find the BCNF of ~(A→B).

A	B	~(A → B)						
T	T	F	T	A∧B	Step (4)	~(A∧B)	Step (5)
T	F	T	F				
F	T	F	T	~A∧B	Step (4)	~(~A∧B)	Step (5)
F	F	F	T	~A∧~B	Step (4)	~(~A∧~B)	Step (5)

Step (6) calls for converting conjunctions into disjunctions. We use one of De Morgan's Laws for this conversion: ~(p∧q)↔(~p∨~q). We also need Double Negation, p↔~~p, which tells us that we can drop any double negations. Using these two equivalences

~(A∧B)	becomes	~A∨~B,
~(~A∧B)	becomes	A∨~B, and
~(~A∧~B)	becomes	A∨B.

Step (7) gives us the BCNF for ~(A→B), which is

(~A∨~B)∧(A∨~B)∧(A∨B).

Since tautologies don't have any false lines in their truth tables, you cannot execute step (2) for tautologies. It follows that tautologies can have a CNF, but they cannot have a BCNF. (A∧B)→(B∧A) is a tautology and thus has no BCNF. It does have a CNF, namely, ((~A∨~B)∨A)∧((~A∨~B)∨B).

Section 6
Logic and Hardware

Physical devices can behave "logically." One can think of the truth table for conjunction, which is not a physical device, as something which produces a true only when it is fed two "trues." It is equally easy to think of a small piece of hardware with two wires leading into it and one wire leading out, which produces an output of a certain kind only when it receives inputs of that kind on both wires leading in to the hardware. The device behaves just like the truth table for conjunction. Such a device is commonly called a *logic gate*. The logic gate that behaves like conjunction is called an *AND gate*. The standard way of representing an AND gate is given below.

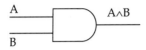

The logic gate for negation is called an *inverter*. It yields the opposite (assuming there are just two kinds of inputs, such as high- and low-level current) of whatever is fed into it. If it receives a high-level input, it produces a low one, and vice versa. The representation for an inverter is

The logic gate for inclusive disjunction produces a high-level output when it receives a high-level input on either of the wires leading into it or on both input wires. This is called an *OR gate* and is represented by

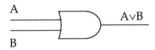

There is no special representation for implication, since an "implication-gate" can be constructed with an inverter and an OR gate. This is possible because of the logical equivalence between p→q and ~p∨q.

In the previous section, it was shown that we can construct any statement in propositional logic using negation, conjunction, and disjunction. It follows that we need at most three basic logic gates. As an illustration, let us construct a complex gate which will behave as the truth table for equivalence behaves. Note that the OR gate below will produce an output whenever it receives either the pairing of p∧q or the pairing of ~p∧~q. Recall that the truth table for equivalence yields an equivalence whenever both p and q are true or whenever they are both false.

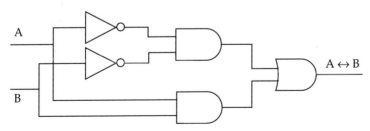

Given De Morgan's laws (introduced in the last section), any or-statement can be converted into an and-statement. That is,

(p∨q)↔~(~p∧~q)

If you doubt this, check the truth table of this equivalence. You will find it is a tautology. Since we have a way of reducing or-statements to and-statements, we can dispense with OR gates and do everything with inverters and AND gates. It would seem we have finally hit rock bottom in eliminating logical operators. Apparently, we need a minimum of two basic pieces of hardware in the construction of logical circuitry. Surprisingly, however, this is mistaken. We can get by with one piece of hardware. This piece is called a *NAND gate*, and it is possible to do all logical calculations with NAND gates alone. NAND gates are represented as

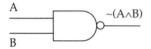

A
~(A∧B)
B

In order to show that NAND gates can represent any logical calculation, we must show that every fundamental logical expression can be represented in terms of ~(p∧q). Every other expression is constructed from these fundamental expressions.

There are only five fundamental operators: ~p, p∧q, p∨q, p→q, and p↔q. The NAND equivalences are given below.

Operator	NAND gate replacement
~p	~(p∧p)
p∧q	~(~(p∧q)∧~(p∧q))
p∨q	~(~(p∧p)∧~(q∧q))
p→q	~(p∧~(q∧q))
p↔q	~(~(~(p∧~(q∧q))∧(q∧~(p∧p)))∧~(~(p∧~(q∧q))∧(q∧~(p∧p))))

A similar reduction can be performed using negation and disjunction. This yields a NOR gate as the operator with which all logical calculations can be expressed. But given the complexity of such reductions, such as the NAND gate replacement for p↔q, why would anyone want to bother with them? This question may be answered crudely by observing that computers don't care about complexity and that their reliability can be improved by using the same kind of logical component throughout the system. Computers don't mind, so to speak, doing the same kind of operation over and over again.

It has been suggested here that computers are basically "logic machines." How does this view fit with the common belief that computers deal primarily with numbers? Most of us are accustomed to the number system that cycles after ten digits (e.g., 0,1,2,3,4,5,6,7,8,9,10,11 . . .).This is called a base-ten number system. There is, of course, a number system which cycles after two digits (e.g., 00,01,10,11, . . .). It is called the base-two, or binary, system. Although it is not our task in this book to learn binary arithmetic, an illustration from the beginning of such arithmetic will allow us to connect logical operations with arithmetic operations.

Recall that the truth table for exclusive disjunction yields true when either disjunct is true, but yields false when both disjuncts are true or when both are false. There are only two kinds of truth values, T and F. And there are only two binary digits: 0 and 1. Let us then compare the truth table for exclusive disjunction and the basic table for binary addition. As a convenience *for this illustration only* let us adopt 'u' as the symbol for exclusive disjunction:

p	q	puq		A	B	A+B
T	T	F		0	0	0
T	F	T		0	1	1
F	T	T		1	0	1
F	F	F		1	1	10

With the exception of line 4, the two tables have the same structure. Thus, one could begin binary addition with a gate which does exclusive disjunction. What this gate won't do, which binary addition requires, is to take care of the case when two 1's arrive. In this case, there is a 1 which must be carried, as in line 4 under A+B. The carry problem can be solved by adding an AND gate to take care of the left column under A+B in line 4. An EXOR gate and an AND gate in the configuration below constitute what is known as a "half-adder." The EXOR gate corresponds to the truth table for exclusive disjunction. You might note that its truth table is the negation of the truth table for equivalence. Since we have already constructed a set of logic gates for equivalence, all we need for an EXOR gate is to feed the output of the equivalence into an inverter.

We'll now represent each of the binary numbers under A+B with two digits. We'll use the output of the EXOR gate to determine the digit for the column on the right and the output of the AND gate to determine the digit for the left column. The half-adder is represented to the left below and the resulting addition table to the right.

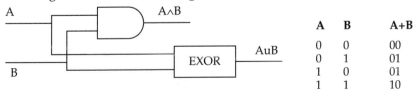

A	B	A+B
0	0	00
0	1	01
1	0	01
1	1	10

In binary arithmetic, '10' represents the number 2 in the base-ten system. A *full adder* is a logic circuit which can handle three columns of digits. It corresponds to a truth table with truth conditions for three separate statements. Such tables require eight lines. Since my purpose here is only to suggest that logical operations underlie arithmetic computations, I'll dispense with further details.

3

Evaluating Arguments in Propositional Logic

Logical consequences are the scarecrows of fools and the beacons of wise men.

T.H. Huxley, *Science and Culture*

Section 1
Proofs and Models

In the neighborhood of 300 B.C., a Greek named Euclid wrote a book that presented in a systematic way the results of the preceding three hundred years of Greek mathematics. Euclid's book, known as *The Elements*, was so nicely organized that for the following two thousand years it was viewed as *the* ideal way in which to present a body of knowledge. Euclid's organization seemed to guarantee a perfect book. Euclid began with definitions of his fundamental terms. He then listed ten basic statements. Today these would be called axioms. The axioms were supposedly so obvious that one would have trouble thinking of alternatives to them. For example, one axiom states that all right angles are equal to one another. Another says, in effect, that between every two points there is a straight line. It seems clear that Euclid intended to begin his book with ten basic truths. The remaining results in the book were called "propositions," and each of these was to be the result of the application of valid rules of reasoning to the axioms and any results which had been derived from the axioms. Valid reasoning is truth-preserving; that is, if the premises of a valid argument are true, then the conclusion must be true. Thus, if Euclid's arguments were valid, each proposition in the book would be true. And how much better could a book be, than to be a book of truths?

In order to critically read Euclid's *Elements,* or any book like it, one must be able to distinguish valid from invalid arguments. We now turn to this task. We will adopt one method, from what is often referred to as **proof theory**, for demonstrating the validity of arguments, and a different method, from what is known as **model theory**, for showing that an argument is invalid. Although validity can also be demonstrated in model theory, the rules of proof of a particular system cannot show certain arguments expressible in the system to be invalid.

Proof construction requires certain rules that permit one to generate new propositions from propositions in hand. One starts a proof with a goal: the proposition to be proved. The *proof* itself is a chain of propositions, each one generated by a rule (except for the axioms), where the last proposition in this chain is that which was to be proved. Constructing a proof is a bit like playing chess where you make a sequence of moves in an effort to reach a desired board configuration. Each move is governed by a rule. The trick is to find a combination of moves that takes you to your goal.

Euclid's *Elements* is proof theoretic. The work shows you what can be produced from certain basic propositions by the use of valid reasoning. The work does not, however, show what cannot be produced from these basic propositions. An argument is invalid when it is possible for the premises of the argument to be true and the conclusion to be false. You simply cannot reach such a conclusion by the use of valid rules. Suppose someone provides you with a set of premises, a conclusion, and some rules with which you are supposed to generate new statements from the premises until you reach the conclusion. Further suppose that the argument you have been given is invalid, but that you don't know this. You begin, using the rules to generate new statements, and three days and many statements later you still have not found a way to generate the conclusion. You are persistent and continue, off and on, to work on this proof for five years without success. The rules won't tell you that you cannot reach the conclusion. Model theory would have shown you that the conclusion was unreachable within the first few minutes of your search.

One of Euclid's axioms is called the *parallel postulate*. One version of this postulate is that given a straight line, L, in a plane and a point, p, in that plane which is not on L, there is exactly one straight line through p which is parallel to L. For some reason, mathematicians following Euclid seemed a bit nervous about the parallel postulate. They tried to turn this axiom into a theorem by constructing an argument with the other nine axioms as premises and the parallel postulate as the conclusion. These attempts, and there were many of them, covered nearly twenty-two hundred years. And during that time no one succeeded in deriving the parallel postulate from the other nine. Apparently, it did not occur to anyone that it was possible for the other nine axioms to be true at the same time the parallel postulate was false. But this, in fact, turned out to be the problem. They had been trying to prove that an invalid argument was valid.

How then is one to show when an argument is invalid? One does this by finding a possible world in which the premises of the argument turn out true and the conclusion turns out false. In other words, one turns to truth tables, or to what is often called *model theory*. One finds a model, a "world," in which the argument doesn't work. And how was this done in the case of the parallel postulate? Suppose we define a straight line as the shortest distance between two points *on* the surface in question. Consider the possible world that is nothing more than the surface of a single sphere. A straight line on this surface will be a great circle or an arc of a great circle. (A great circle is found by passing a plane through the center of the sphere and looking at the intersection of the plane and the surface of the sphere.) Consider any great circle, C, and any point, p, on the surface of the sphere but not on C. There is no great circle passing through p which does not intersect C. Thus, in this possible world there are no parallel lines. Euclid's parallel postulate, which would insist there be one "straight" line through p that does not intersect C, is false in this world. Assuming all the other Euclidean axioms could be true in this world (this admittedly is an oversimplification), we have shown that one cannot validly produce the parallel postulate from the other nine axioms. We have shown this in model theory, not in proof theory.

It is not crucial for what follows that you have understood all the details just given about the parallel postulate. You should understand, however, that proof construction will be reserved for showing that arguments are valid and that model theory (truth-table reasoning) will be reserved for showing that certain arguments are invalid. (Recall that model theory can also be used to demonstrate validity.) Note that neither method *makes* an argument valid or invalid. It is impossible to show a valid argument to be invalid, and equally impossible to show an invalid argument to be valid. The arguments you will face are already valid or invalid. Your task will be to *show* validity or invalidity.

This chapter has been restricted to arguments in propositional logic, that level of logic which deals with simple statements represented by single capital letters, such as A, B, and C, and with complexes of these simples formed with logical connectives, such as ∨, ∧, and →. We'll begin with techniques for showing invalidity, since these are easier to master than techniques of proof construction.

Section 2

Using Truth Tables to Show
That an Argument is Invalid

Consider a simple argument:

If Mary lied, Ed cried.
Ed cried.
Therefore, Mary lied.

If we translate this argument into the notation of propositional logic we get

M→E
E
Therefore, M.

Is this a valid argument, and if not, how can we show that it is not? If the argument is valid, it will be impossible for its premises to be true while its conclusion is false. A truth table tells us what is possible under all truth conditions. So, we need a truth table. But we are accustomed to constructing truth tables for single statements, and the argument before us consists of three statements. We need a way to convert this argument into a single statement. This can be found in a simple description of the argument that says if M→E and E are true, then M is true. M→E and E imply M. In notation, ((M→E)∧E)→M. If we write the truth table for this expression, we can see if the premises ever turn out true on a line where the conclusion has turned out false. If such a line is found, the argument is invalid. If there is no such line, the argument is valid. Let us see:

M	E	((M → E)	∧	E)	→	M
T	T	T	T	T	T	T
T	F	F	F	F	T	T
F	T	T	T	T	F	F
F	F	T	F	F	T	F

On line 3, or in possible world 3, both premises turn out true and the conclusion turns out false. Thus there is a world in which this argument does not work. The argument is invalid. If someone asks you for a demonstration of the invalidity of the argument, you only need say "just check the case where M is false and E is true." That is, check line 3.

Recall that a valid argument is one the truth table of which is a tautology and that an invalid argument has a truth table which calculates to false on at least one line. Let us review the process for representing an argument as a single implication statement:

- *Step 1.* Conjoin all of the premises on a single line, i.e., the first premise followed by an ∧, followed by the second premise, followed by an ∧, followed by the third premise . . . , until you have run out of premises.
- *Step 2.* Put parentheses around the big conjunction you have formed in Step 1. Write an implication sign, →, after the parenthesis farthest to the right and write the conclusion after the implication sign.
- *Step 3.* Construct a truth table for the line you have formed. If this table is a tautology, you've got a valid argument. If not, the argument is invalid.

Let's try another argument:

1. A→B
2. ~A
Therefore, ~B

Step 1 above yields (A→B)∧~A.
Step 2 produces ((A→B)∧~A)→~B.
Step 3 calls for a truth table. This is given below:

A	B	((A → B)	∧ ~A)	→ ~B
T	T	T	F F	T F
T	F	F	F F	T T
F	T	T	T T	F F
F	F	T	T T	T T

Once again it is line 3 that has calculated to false. Since there is a line in which the premises are true and the conclusion is false, the argument is invalid. The truth tables of some invalid arguments will have more than one line that calculates to false. Any one of these lines is enough to show the argument invalid.

Now suppose you're armed with your truth-table method for detecting invalidity and you encounter the following argument: (Someone has saved you the trouble of translating it into logical notation, so you don't really know what it is about. But you do know how to test it for invalidity.)

1. C∨~C
2. C→(I∨~D)
3. I→(L→T)
4. T
5. ~D→~P
6. P
7. ~C→~M
8. M
Therefore, ~L

This is a bit messier than our previous examples, but if we follow steps 1 through 3 we can get the job done. Following steps 1 and 2 we'll conjoin the eight premises, add an implication sign, and then add the conclusion. The result is the single line given below.

$$((C \lor {\sim}C) \land (C \rightarrow (I \lor {\sim}D)) \land (I \rightarrow (L \rightarrow T)) \land T \land ({\sim}D \rightarrow {\sim}P) \land P \land ({\sim}C \rightarrow {\sim}M) \land M) \rightarrow {\sim}L$$

Step 3 requires us to write the truth table for this expression. We begin by setting forth all of the possible combinations of truth values, or all of the possible worlds, for this expression. There are seven different statements, or letters, in the argument. I'll pick them in the order in which they show up in the proof:

C	I	D	L	T	P	M
T	T	T	T	T	T	T
T	T	T	T	T	T	F
T	T	T	T	T	F	T

But wait. Since this table has seven different letters, it will have 2 raised-to-the-seventh-power different lines (i.e., 128 lines). I've done no more above than lay out the truth conditions for the first three lines. There is no way I'm going to write out a 128-line table. Even if I did, I'd surely make a mistake when running through the calculation. There must be a better method than this for showing arguments to be invalid. And so there is.

If we return to our simpler example involving Mary and Ed, we find that line 3, where the premises were true and the conclusion false, did all of the work for us. In showing invalidity we need a single counterexample, a single line. Why then write out a whole table if just one line in the table will get the job done? But how can we find a line which will get the job done without writing out the whole table?

Well, we know something about what such a line will be like. We know that it must be a line in which all premises are true and in which the conclusion is false. An invalid argument is one for which there is at least one possible world where the premises are true and the conclusion is false. Why not, then, try to find that possible world by seeing if we can make the premises true and the conclusion false at the same time?

"What do you mean *'make* the premises true' and 'make *the conclusion false'*? One cannot dictate what is true and what is false. In a particular world, such as the one in which we live, one cannot make a certain claim, such as 'Our earth has one moon,' false by declaring that it is false." These observations are correct, but we must recall that truth tables are about all possible worlds. There is a possible world, and it turns out to be our world, in which the earth has one moon. There is another possible world, not the one we know, in which the earth does not have one moon. Truth tables capture both possibilities. So the question before us is, is there a possible world in which the conclusion is false and the premises are true? There is a possible world where the conclusion of the eight-premise argument above is false. It is the world (or the line on the truth table) where L is true. In this world, ~L turns out false. Therefore, "making ~L false" simply means "finding the condition under which ~L turns out false." It is only under this condition that one might show that the argument is invalid.

To clarify the previous point, suppose (just for a moment) that the conclusion of the argument was Av~A. Av~A is a tautology and thus cannot be false. So how do you make the conclusion of such an argument false? The obvious answer is that you cannot. Any argument which has a tautology for a conclusion is automatically valid. You just can't show the premises of such an argument to be true and the conclusion to be false. But ~L is not a tautology. It is contingent. It turns out false whenever L is true. Since we are looking for a case where the conclusion is false (and the premises are true) to show invalidity, we begin with a case where ~L calculates to false.

Thus far, we have "made" the conclusion false by "letting" L be true. Since this is the only way, in this case, to make ~L false, we are stuck with this assignment. Wherever L appears in the argument it must be labelled true. But we have not committed ourselves to truth-value assignments to any other letters in the argument. Can we find some combination of assignments to those remaining six letters that makes each and every premise come out true? If we can, we will have found a line in the truth table in which all premises are true and the conclusion is false. We will have shown the argument to be invalid.

There are eight premises. Which do we go to first? Why not go to the simplest premises first, such as lines 4, 6, and 8? Line 4 will turn out true only if we make T true. In assigning a true to T in line 4, we make that assignment for any other occurrence of T in the argument. If we move to line 6, we find we must make P true. And we must make M true in line 8. At this point, we have used up four of our seven options by assigning truth values to L, T, P, and M. We bought something with these assignments: the conclusion is false, and premises 4, 6, and 8 are true. We no longer have to worry about four of the nine lines in the argument. We also have a lot of information to plug into the other lines in the argument. Keep in mind that our remaining task is to see that the remaining premises turn out true.

Line 1, Cv~C, is tautology and cannot be false. So we can ignore it. The next least complex lines are 5 and 7. Line 5 is ~D→~P. We have already been forced to make P true. Accordingly, ~P in line 5 is false. The only way line 5 can turn out true is by ~D turning out false. (Check the last line in the truth table for →.) Thus D must be true.

We find a similar situation in line 7, where ~M must be false because we had to make M true. Thus, ~C must be false, and C must be true. This leaves us with lines 2 and 3. All other premises are now true. We have also given truth values to every letter but I.

Line 2 is C→(Iv~D). Since we have been forced to make C and D true, and therefore ~D false, we must make I true for line 2 to turn out true. We have now used up all of our options on assigning truth values. Do these assignments force line 3, I→(L→T), to be true? Happily, I, L, and T have all been made true. That means line 3 is true. Our assignments lead to eight true premises and a false conclusion. We can show this by plugging the assignments into the argument and calculating the result for each line. This set of assignments (truth values) constitutes a counterexample against the argument in question. These assignments represent a possible world in which the argument doesn't work, a line in that one-hundred-twenty-eight-line truth table that calculates to false. Mercifully, we did not have to write out the entire truth table to find such a line.

When an argument is invalid, the method sketched in the example above will show it is. The "showing" consists of providing the truth values which force the conclusion to be false and the premises to be true. In a valid argument, this showing is impossible.

In each of the three examples of invalid arguments we have seen, there was exactly one truth-value assignment which forced the conclusion to be false. Obviously cases will arise where there is more than one way in which the conclusion can turn out false. Which of these should be chosen when trying to show that the argument is invalid? The answer is simple. Choose an assignment which doesn't stop you from making all of the premises true. But how does one know which assignment this is? Again, the answer is simple. Proceed by trial and error until you find an assignment which will get the job done. For example:

1. A↔B
2. B↔C
3. C↔D
Therefore, A∧B

One can make A∧B false by making A false, or B false, or both A and B false. In showing an argument to be invalid, we must show that there is a way to make the conclusion false while making the premises true. Suppose, in the case before us, we make A false and B true. Certainly that will make the conclusion false, but it also makes the first premise false. Similarly, making A true and B false will make the conclusion false, but it will also make the first premise false. Only by making both A and B false do we force the conclusion to be false and the first premise to be true. We can make lines 2 and 3 true by making both C and D false. We show this argument to be invalid by making A, B, C and D false.

As noted earlier, there may be several sets of truth-value assignments which get the job done. That is, there may be several lines in the truth table for the argument that calculate to false. Any of these lines is sufficient to show the argument to be invalid. Therefore, there may be several correct answers to some of the problems in the following set of exercises. Do each of the exercises to assure yourself you understand this section. Check your results against the answers in the back of the book. Hereafter in this text, I'll replace the 'therefore' before the conclusion with '//.'

Exercises

Show that each of the following arguments is invalid by coming up with a set of truth values which force the conclusion to be false and each of the premises to be true:

1. A∨B	6. A→B	11. A∨~A	16. (P∨Q)→R
~A	A∨C	B∨~B	R→(S∧T)
//~B	C→D	//Z	//P→~S
	//E→B		
2. A∨B	7. ~(M∧N)	12. A	17. A↔(B∧C)
//A	//M∨~N	B	(D∨E)→A
		//C	//A∨E
3. A→B	8. ~(C→D)	13. P→Q	18. (A→B)∧(C→D)
B→~A	C→E	Q↔(R∧S)	//(A∨C)∧(B∨D)
//A	E↔F	P→S	
	//C∧D	//Q→T	
4. A→B	9. A→(B→C)	14. ~(A∧B)	19. ~(D∨C)
B	//(A→B)→C	~(C∧~B)	~(A→E)
C→D		~(~C∧A)	(D∨E)↔F
~C		//A	G→F
//A∧~D			//~((A∧B)→C)
5. (P∧Q)→R	10. A→B	15. J→K	20. B∨(D∨E)
R→S	B→C	K→L	A→((C∧D)∨E)
S→T	C→D	~L∨M	~(A∨B)
T→U	D→E	N∨~M	D→~(A→C)
//P→U	E→F	//N∨J	(C∧D)→~A
	F→A		//~E
	//A		

The Method of Resolution

The method of resolution, commonly known in logic as the method of truth-trees or semantic tableaux, is a natural outgrowth of the short-cut method just shown for demonstrating the invalidity of arguments. The method of resolution shows whether an argument is valid or invalid as follows.

(1) List all the premises of the argument and add to the list the negation of the conclusion. Note that our short-cut truth-table reasoning method began with the plan of showing that the conclusion could be made false while the premises could be made true.

(2) Then see if it is possible to make all the lines in this list true, *without generating a contradiction*. If every attempt to make all the lines true leads to a contradiction, the argument is valid. If at least one branch of the tree does not produce a contradiction, the argument is invalid.

Examples will clarify this procedure. Let us begin with a valid argument:

1. ~A∨B
2. B→C
// 3. ~C→~A

Following step (1) above, we list:

1.   ~A∨B
2.   B→C
3.   ~(~C→~A)

In following step (2) we must list the conditions which will make line 3 come out true (i.e., A and ~C). In this case, no other assignments will do the job:

4.   A
5.   ~C

Having made line 3 true, we can "check it off." You may put a check next to it if you like, which tells us we don't have to worry about it any more. Let us move on to line 2. What will make B→C true? Making C true will do it, as will making B false (i.e., ~B). We have ~C in line 5, so we list the branching paths from ~C in line 6:

5.   ~C
            ╱ ╲
6.   ~B   C
               X

We may now check off line 2 and note that the branch from ~C to C contains a contradiction. So we close that branch, by placing an X under C. Only line 1, ~A∨B, remains. This line can be made true, if we have either ~A or B. So line 6 branches into line 7 as follows:

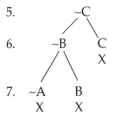

5.   ~C
               ╱ ╲
6.   ~B   C
        ╱ ╲   X
7.   ~A   B
     X   X

The path from ~B to B can be closed, as can the path to ~A because of the A in line 4. The tree is now complete because we have listed all conditions under which our initial lines (1–3) come out true. The tree would not be complete if any letter in the original argument had not been brought out either as itself or as its negation. Whether one brings out the letter or its negation depends on which option forces the statement in which it occurs to be true. Since all paths closed in the case above, the argument is valid. Every attempt to make the premises and the negation of conclusion true leads to contradiction.

Now let us consider an invalid argument.

      1. ~A∨B
      2. B→C
// 3. C→A

We begin as before, listing the premises and the negation of the conclusion:

1.   ~A∨B
2.   B→C
3.   ~(C→A)

We now proceed to list the condition under which line 3 is true (i.e., ~A and C):

4.   ~A

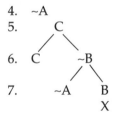

We check off 3 and list the conditions for 2. We check off 2 and list the conditions for 1. The path from ~B to B closes, but the paths from ~A and C do not close. The argument is invalid. Note that C and ~A make the premises true and conclusion false in the original argument.

The method of resolution is a standard theorem-proving technique in computer science. We now turn to another approach to theorem proving, one that displays more clearly the process of deductive thinking. We will use a system known as natural deduction. A few introductory remarks are in order before we present natural deduction.

Section 3

Proving That an Argument Is Valid
in Propositional Logic

Constructing a proof is like playing a game. When playing a game, such as a board game, one is given some pieces, some rules for how one is permitted to move these pieces about, and an objective. In chess, for example, one is given a board, sixteen white pieces for one player, sixteen black pieces for the other player, rules for moving these pieces, and the objective of capturing the opponent's piece called the king. In logic proofs, one is given some initial formulas (which represent propositions), a set of rules which permit one to generate new formulas from those given, and the objective of generating a particular formula by using the rules on the formulas. At the beginning of a typical proof, you will be given three things: initial formulas (premises), an objective (a conclusion to be reached), and a list of rules for generating new formulas from those in hand.

The rules for generating new formulas from those in hand are commonly called *rules of inference.* Some of these rules have been known for a long time and have special names. For example, the rule of *disjunctive syllogism* (DS) is so old that an ancient Greek logician claimed that even dogs know it. The rule must be old, since anything known to dogs is likely to have been known to humans before the advent of writing. The rule is simple. If I know there are only two paths to follow and that I shouldn't follow one of these, then I should follow the other one. Or, to return to propositional logic, if p∨q and ~p, then q.

Disjunctive syllogism should be viewed as an instruction which you may use. As an instruction it reads: If you have in hand (either as a premise or something you derived from premises) a formula (a line) of the form p∨q, and if you also have in hand another line of the form ~p, then you are permitted to (but you don't have to) write a new line of the form q. Note that DS has been expressed as an argument form. The p in p∨q and ~p is a slot into which many different statements may fall. The same is true for q. Thus, given premises

1.   (A↔C)∨D
2.   ~(A↔C)

one can use DS to generate D. A↔C fell into the p slot, and D fell into the q slot. We can also use DS on

1.   M∨N
2.   ~M

to generate N.

Suppose you possessed only the rule of DS and were confronted with the following problem:

1. Av~B
2. BvC
3. ~A //C

One understands that lines 1, 2, and 3 are premises and that the //C to the right of line 3 is the line to be generated by using the rules (in this case DS). One is not permitted to treat C as a premise. The proof proceeds after line 3 as follows:

4. ~B 1,3 DS
5. C   2,4 DS

Line 4, ~B, came from a use of DS on lines 1 and 3. This is precisely what "1,3 DS" means on line 4. Each move in a proof (each new line) must have a *justification*. "1,3 DS" is the justification for line 4. The justification for a line tells which lines you came from and which rule you used on those lines to generate the line in question.

The justifications we require in these proofs capture the concept of *effectiveness*. An effective proof procedure is one which can be checked mechanically. No creative thinking is required. You look at the formula in question (the question is where the formula came from), and to its right you see, in effect, "This formula came from lines n and m by use of, say, the rule DS." You need only look at lines n and m and check the rule DS to see if this is true. A rigorous logical or mathematical proof is effective, or mechanically checkable. This notion of rigor has developed during the past one hundred years. Much mathematics prior to 1879 put a great deal of stress on the intellectual powers of the reader. It should be noted that much advanced contemporary mathematics has not been rendered mechanically checkable. Why bother with the notion of effectiveness? It is the best means of being sure that you haven't made any mistakes.

What Justifies Rules of Inference?

How do we know that DS is a "good" rule of inference? We want rules that generate valid arguments. We want rules that will guarantee true conclusions from true premises. DS is such a rule. If pvq is true and if ~p is true, there is no way q won't be true. We know this because the truth table for DS is a tautology. There is no line in its table which calculates to false. If you doubt this, simply write the truth table for $((p \lor q) \land \neg p) \rightarrow q$. The truth table for every rule we will use in this section is a tautology. Such rules are truth preserving; if you begin with truths, they will generate truths.

How Many Rules Are Needed and Which Rules Are Needed?

We want a set of rules which can generate any valid argument which may arise in propositional logic. Although one can do this with a very small number of rules, most logic texts use more than the minimum necessary to get the job done. The question of how many rules of inference are used and which particular rules are used does not usually concern someone who is being introduced to logic. The question is raised here, even before you've seen a set of rules, to indicate that the selection is guided by certain principles. These principles involve trade-offs (e.g., the smaller the set of rules, the longer the average proof). The following illustration will introduce a few of the rules we will use and should provide you with some sense about the problem of choosing a set of rules.

Most systems of logic include the following rules:

Double Negation (DN) $p \leftrightarrow \sim\sim p$	This rule permits you to drop two "nots" that apply to the same formula or to introduce two "nots" in front of any formula.
Implication (Impl) $(p \rightarrow q) \leftrightarrow (\sim p \vee q)$	This rule tells us that $p \rightarrow q$ and $\sim p \vee q$ are interchangeable—they are logically equivalent.
Hypothetical Syllogism (HS) $p \rightarrow q$ $q \rightarrow r$ $//p \rightarrow r$	This rule says that if you have in hand a line of the form $p \rightarrow q$, and another line of the form $q \rightarrow r$, then you may write a new line of the form $p \rightarrow r$.
Simplification (Simp) $p \wedge q$ $//p$ or $//q$	This rule says that if you have a line of the form $p \wedge q$, then you may write p on a separate line or write q on a separate line.
Transposition (Trans) $(\sim p \rightarrow q) \leftrightarrow (\sim q \rightarrow \sim p)$	This rule tells you that $p \rightarrow q$ and $\sim q \rightarrow \sim p$ are logically equivalent. You may rewrite a line on which one of them appears, replacing one with the other.

The following rule is omitted from many formulations of logic:

Constructive Dilemma (CD) $(p \rightarrow q) \wedge (r \rightarrow s)$ $p \vee r$ $//q \vee s$	If you have lines of the forms $(p \rightarrow q) \wedge (r \rightarrow s)$ and $p \vee r$, you may write a new line of the form $q \vee s$.

A comparison of the following proofs shows the tension between keeping the number of rules down and reducing the number of lines in a proof:

1. (A→B)∧(C→D)		1. (A→B)∧(C→D)	
2. A∨C //B∨D		2. A∨C //B∨D	
3. B∨D 1,2 CD		3. A→B	1 Simp
		4. C→D	1 Simp
		5. ~B→~A	3 Trans
		6. ~~A∨C	2 DN
		7. ~A→C	6 Impl
		8. ~B→C	5,7 HS
		9. ~B→D	8,4 HS
		10. ~~B∨D	9 Impl
		11. B∨D	10 DN

The right-hand proof shows that one can move from lines 1 and 2 to line 11 without the use of CD. Thus we can dispense with CD as a separate rule. However, in so doing, certain proofs become considerably longer.

The truth table for CD, like the truth table for all rules, is a tautology. Why not, then, take any pairing of premises and conclusion that has a tautology for a truth table, and count this pairing as a rule of inference? For example, although it is not obvious, the truth table for

~(A→(B→(C→D)))
//C

is a tautology. We could take the form of this argument to be another rule. The number of possible rules is effectively infinite. No one could state, much less remember, all possible rules. Since all rules can be checked with a truth table, we could justify every move in propositional logic by what one logician has termed "Rule T": the premise-conclusion pair have a truth table which is a tautology. There is a seeming economy with Rule T: you only need one rule. There is, unfortunately, a lot of truth-table checking required. A practical compromise seems in order. We don't want too few rules because proofs become too long. We don't want too many rules because they would be hard to keep track of and we would be constantly checking their validity with truth tables. Such a compromise has been reached. It is called *natural deduction.*

The idea behind natural deduction is to find a set of rules people commonly use when reasoning (hence the "natural") which can demonstrate the validity of any argument that is valid. The central feature of a **natural deduction system** is that the set of rules alone are enough to generate the system. Other systems require a combination of axioms and rules of inference. The last two remarks will become more meaningful when you have seen the rule of conditional proof, a rule with which you can generate valid results even when you have no premises.

The names of the rules in natural deduction systems vary. For example, disjunctive syllogism is often called "or-elimination" because the rule permits you to break out, on a separate line, the second term of an or-statement.

There is some flexibility in the selection of a set of rules for a natural-deduction system, but the selection is not entirely arbitrary. Each rule must have a truth table which is a tautology. The set of rules selected must be capable of generating any valid argument in propositional logic. The rules we will use are given below. Two additional rules, which require more discussion, will be treated later.

THE RULES

Conditional Rules		**Equivalence Rules**	
p→q p //q	Modus Ponens (MP)	(p∨q)↔(q∨p) (p∧q)↔(q∧p)	Commutation (Comm)
p→q ~q //~p	Modus Tollens (MT)	(p∨(q∨r))↔((p∨q)∨r) (p∧(q∧r))↔((p∧q)∧r)	Association (Assoc)
p→q q→r //p→r	Hypothetical Syllogism (HS)	(p∨(q∧r))↔((p∨q)∧(p∨r)) (p∧(q∨r))↔((p∧q)∨(p∧r))	Distribution (Dist)
pvq ~p //q	Disjunctive Syllogism (DS)	~(p∨q)↔(~p∧~q) ~(p∧q)↔(~p∨~q)	DeMorgan's Laws (DeM)
		(p→q)↔(~p∨q)	Implication (Impl)
p q //p∧q	Conjunction (Conj)	(p↔q)↔((p→q)∧(q→p)) (p↔q)↔((p∧q)∨(~p∧~q))	Equivalence (Equiv)

p∧q
//p
//q
	Simplification
	(Simp)
		(p→q)↔(~q→~p)	Transposition

		((p∧q)→r)↔(p→(q→r))	Exportation (Exp)
p //p∨q	Addition	p↔(p∨p) p↔(p∧p)	Tautology (Taut)
p→q //p→(p∧q)	Absorption	p↔~~p	Double Negation (DN)

There are some important differences between the rules in the left-hand column (the conditional rules) and the right-hand column (the equivalence rules).

(1) The conditional rules are "one-way" rules. They are always read, "If you have in hand the conditions listed above the '//' sign, then you may write the expression after the '//' sign." You cannot reverse this procedure. For example, the rule of Modus Ponens says that if you already have two lines, one of the form p→q and the other of the form p, then you may write a new line of the form q. It does not say that if you have q you can write p or

p→q. In contrast, the equivalence rules (right-hand column) are "two-way" rules. For example, the rule of implication says if you have an expression of the form p→q, then you may rewrite that expression on a new line as ~p∨q. It also says that if you have an expression of the form ~p∨q you may rewrite that expression on a new line as p→q. That is, you may read the rule from left to right or from right to left.

(2) The conditional rules cannot be used on a part of line. So, modus ponens (MP) can be used on the following pairs of lines:

A→B	(C∧D)→E	A→(B∨C)	(M∨N)→(R→S)	A→(Z↔Z)
A	C∧D	A	M∨N	A

to produce:

B	E	B∨C	R→S	(Z↔Z)

But modus ponens cannot be used on the following lines:

(a)	(A→B)∨C	(b)	C∧(D→C)	(c)	(M∨N)→(R→S)
	A→B		D		R

The first line of (a) is primarily a disjunction. The form for modus ponens calls for an implication. Simply compare the form given in (a) with the form for the first two lines of the modus ponens rule:

p∨q   vs.   p→q
p   p

To use a rule on certain lines, the form of those lines *must* fit the form of the rule. The first line of (b) is basically a conjunction. Modus ponens cannot be used on conjunctions, even though one of the conjuncts is an implication. (c) is basically an implication. But the second line of (c) is not the antecedent of this implication. The modus ponens rule says, "Show me a line which is basically an implication and show me another line which is the first part of this implication." The second condition is not satisfied in (c).

In contrast, the equivalence rules may be used on a part of a line. They are, in effect, substitution rules. You pull an expression out and substitute in its place a logical equivalent. You are doing nothing but changing the form of expression. You are not adding anything to a line or breaking anything out of the line. With equivalence rules you may change the form of an entire line or the form of a part of line. The following example shows equivalence rules at work:

1. (~B→~A)∧(~B∨A)   // A↔B
2. (A→B)∧(~B∨A)   1 Trans   [on ~B→~A)]

3. $(A{\to}B){\wedge}(B{\to}A)$ 2 Impl   [on ~BvA]
4. $A{\leftrightarrow}B$ 3 Equiv   [on the entire line]

Note that when one makes the substitution the unchanged remainder of the line is carried along. Adopt the following convention to avoid errors: Each new line is to come from one use of one rule.

Checking a Proof vs. Constructing a Proof

You will find it fairly easy to follow someone else's use of these rules. I am about to offer several examples of proofs. It won't take long before you have no difficulty in checking such proofs. You look at a new line and then at its justification. The justification tells you which lines the new one came from and which rule was used on those lines. You go back, check the lines, check to see that the rule used actually fits those lines, and satisfy yourself that the new line was legally produced. However, there will come a time when you are asked to construct a proof. The ease with which you will have learned to check proofs may mislead you into thinking it is just as easy to construct a proof. In fact, proof construction is harder.

In proofchecking you follow what someone else has already done. In proof construction you must decide on your own which rule to use in which situation. There is no rule that tells the order in which to use the rules. So even when you know all the rules, there will be no set of rules that tells you when to use them. This situation is similar to playing chess. It is easy to learn the basic rules of chess. It is difficult to know which move to make (which rule to use) in a given situation. Chess would not be interesting if there were a set of rules which told you what to do in each situation. If there were such rules, we could dispense with you as a chess player. Similarly, logic would not be interesting if there were a set of rules which constructed proofs for you. In either case, a set of rules for when to use the rules would amount to a computer program which would play for you. In that case, who needs you?

So, follow my proofs and then be prepared for a little frustration when I ask you to construct proofs of your own. This frustration is a part of the learning process. If you have patience and persist, you will learn and the frustration will disappear. The examples below will be followed by an explanation of two additional rules of inference: *conditional proof* (CP) and *indirect proof* (IP). You may use any of the rules introduced so far in working through the exercises at the end of the chapter.

Examples

(1) 1. A→B
    2. B→C   //A→C
    3. A→C   1,2 HS

How did I know to use HS on lines 1 and 2? I am familiar enough with the rules to notice that 1 and 2 fit the form required by HS. A falls into the p slot, B into the q slot, and C into the r slot. (See the rule.)

(2) 1. (D↔E)→((F∧G)∨H)
    2. ((F∧G)∨H)→Z   //(D↔E)→Z
    3. (D↔E)→Z   1,2 HS

Keep in mind that HS is an argument form. In this case, D↔E fills the p slot in p→q and in p→r. (F∧G)∨H fills the q slot in both p→q and q→r. Z, of course, fills the r slot.

(3) 1. B→C
    2. A→B   //A→C
    3. A→C   2,1 HS

The order of the lines makes no difference. You can use HS on lines 1 and 2, reading line 2 first.

(4) 1. −A∨B
    2. B→C   //A→C
    3. A→B   1 Impl
    4. A→C   3,2 HS

The only difference between this problem and (1) above is that the logical equivalent of A→B, namely ~A∨B, is on line 1. Thus, you go hunting for an equivalence rule which permits you to arrive at a form where you can use HS. In general, the conditional rules break things out of lines or build up lines. The equivalence rules allow you to change the form of lines or parts of lines so that you arrive at a form where the conditional rules may be used.

(5) 1. (A→B)∧(B→C)   //A→C
    2. A→B   1 Simp
    3. B→C   1 Simp
    4. A→C   2,3 HS

This is also like (1), but since HS is a "two-line" rule you cannot use it on line 1 alone. It says, "Show me a line of the form p→q and another line of the form q→r. Then you may write a new line of the form p→r." Note that MP, MT, DS, and Conj are also two-line rules. So you should never construct a proof where a line is justified by something like "5 MP."

(6) 1. J∨K
   2. ~J //K
   3. K   1,2 DS

All you have to do is find the DS rule (or remember it) to complete this proof.

(7) 1. K∨J
   2. ~J
   3. J∨K   1 Comm
   4. K   3,2 DS

If you examine carefully the form of DS you find that it demands the negation of the left disjunct in the or-statement. I know this is being picky. It is obvious that K∨J and J∨K mean the same thing. It is obvious, but we are involved in a rule-bound activity. The rule says that you need the negation of the *left* disjunct. That sends you to the list of equivalence rules, looking for a rule which permits you to switch terms about "or" signs. Sure enough, there is such a rule: Commutation. You would use this rule in your head even if you didn't write down a step for it. We ask that you write down every move you make.

(8) 1. A→(B∨C)
   2. ~(B∨C) //~A
   3. ~A   1,2 MT

All you have to do is find MT and not fall into the trap of thinking that the q slot can only be filled with a single letter.

(9) 1. A→(B∨C)
   2. ~B∧~C //~A
   3. ~(B∨C)   2 DeM
   4. ~A   1,3 MT

"Gee, Fred, this looks a lot like the last problem. I'll bet whoever made this up just looked for an equivalent for line 2 in (8)."

(10) 1. A //A∨Z
    2. A∨Z   1 Add

Addition (Add) strikes some people as illegal. It looks as though the rule permits you to establish something from nothing, such as Z in the above problem. However, addition simply says that if p is true, p∨q is true. Given the truth table for ∨, the rule is absolutely correct. Note that in the proof above the result is not Z alone, but A∨Z.

(11) 1. (A∨B)→C
    2. A //C
    3. A∨B   2 Add
    4. C   1,3 MP

If you have accepted Add as legitimate, why not use it? You need an A∨B to go with line 1 so you can use MP to produce C. But you were only given A in line 2.

Add comes to the rescue.

(12) 1. C→(D→E)
    2. ~C //C→D
    3. ~C∨D   2 Add
    4. C→D   4 Impl

If you were doing this problem on your own, you probably would have started with the belief that you must use all of the premises given when constructing the proof. Thus you might have tried to do something with line 1. Since line 1 is an implication, you might have tried to break it up with MP or MT. But you need C (not ~C) to use MP on line 1, and the ~C in line 2 will not help you to use MT. You might have tried using Impl on the →signs in line 1, thereby changing the expression to ~C∨(~D∨E). DS breaks up disjunctions, but ~C in line 2 won't let you use DS. You need ~~C (or C) and you don't have it. Thus, it turns out that line 1 is of no use in reaching the conclusion of this proof. The more time you spend trying to use it, the longer it will take you to finish the proof. How are you supposed to know this? Well, there aren't too many things you can do with line 1. We tried the obvious things, such as MP, MT, and DS, with no success. *Suggestion:* Change the form of the conclusion (as scratch work on the side) and then look for a relation between the remaining premise and the conclusion. The conclusion, C→D, is equivalent to ~C∨D. Add will take you from ~C to ~C∨D. Changing the form of the conclusion will often reveal a connection between the premises and the conclusion which is not evident in the problem as presented. One changes form through the equivalence rules.

(13) 1. A∨(B∨C)
    2. ~C //A∨B
    3. (A∨B)∨C   1 Assoc
    4. C∨(A∨B)   2 Comm
    5. A∨B   4,2 DS

DS breaks up or-statements, but it calls for the negation of the left disjunct. Since C in line 1 is on the right, it must be moved to the left by Assoc and Comm.

(14) 1. A∨(~B∧~C)
    2. C //A
    3. (A∨~B)∧(A∨~C) 1 Dist
    4. A∨~C   3 Simp
    5. ~C∨A   4 Comm
    6. ~~C   2 DN
    7. A   5,6 DS

Find a form from which you can simplify (Simp). So use Dist to form a conjunction. Pull out the part with ~C in it. Commute to get ~C on the left side and find the negation of ~C. DS finishes the proof.

This proof could have proceeded in another way. There are usually many different ways to do a proof. A valid proof requires a chain of lines, all produced by the rules, the last line of which is the conclusion. You might take, on some problem, eight steps to reach a conclusion which could be reached in three steps. Your proof, if you used the rules correctly at each step, will be correct. (14) could have ended as follows:

6. C→A	5 Impl
7. A	6,2 MP

Or the proof could have been done as follows:

3. A∨~(B∨C)	1 DeM
4. C∨B	2 Add
5. B∨C	4 Comm
6. ~~(B∨C)	5 DN
7. ~(B∨C)∨A	3 Comm
8. A	7,6 DS

(15) 1. A∨B
    2. B→C //~A→C
    3. ~~A∨B   1 DN
    4. ~A→B   3 Impl
    5. ~A→C   4,2 HS

Looks like a job for HS. The conclusion is a conditional, as is the second premise. The first premise is a disjunction which can be converted to a conditional by Impl. The problem with the conversion in this proof is that Impl calls for ~p∨q, which then may be replaced by p→q. Line 1 has no negation sign. The only way to introduce negations is by DN, and this rule requires they be introduced two at a time. So we replaced A in line 1 with ~~A in line 3, while carrying over '∨B' of course. We then used Impl, substituting ~A in the p slot and B in the q slot, to arrive at line 4.

(16) 1. A
    2. ~A //Z
    3. A∨Z   1 Add
    4. Z   4,3 DS

Lines 1 and 2 are the parts of a contradiction. Contradictions can never yield *sound* reasoning, since a sound argument must have true premises. Obviously, lines 1 and 2 cannot both be true. From this it follows that an argument with contradictory premises *must* be valid. For an argument to be invalid, it must be possible for each and every premise to be true and for the conclusion to be false. An argument with contradictory premises cannot, then, be invalid. But why on earth would anyone construct an argument with contradictory premises? There are a variety of reasons. First, someone may want to bug you. Second, someone may want to trick you. It is not inconceivable that a politician would bury a contradiction in an argument and proceed to demonstrate validly a certain conclusion not available without that contradiction. The argument would be in English and the contradiction would not be nearly as visible as it is in lines 1 and 2 of (16). Example (16) shows that from a contradiction *anything* can be proved. Note that the conclusion, Z, of (16) could have been any expression at all. The proof would have gone through the same two steps: add the conclusion to one side of the contradiction and use DS with the other side.

A third cause of contradictions is the sheer complexity of certain formal systems. Humans have an inclination to generate systems which cover an enormous amount of ground. Sometimes they produce something in one part of the system that contradicts something introduced in another part of the system—without realizing it. This, of course, is undesirable, but it happens. When contradictions are discovered in such systems, steps are taken to eliminate them. Contradictions are feared in such systems precisely because of the proof in (16). With a contradiction, any result, including the most difficult conjectures in mathematics, can be generated in two steps (Add and DS). This would trivialize mathematics and logic. However, if you ever take a logic course and someone is foolish enough to supply you with contradictory premises, you are two steps from finishing the proof once you find that contradiction.

Fourteen of the eighteen rules have been used thus far. It is only fair that the other four, plus the second version of Equiv, receive some space:

(17) 1. $A \rightarrow B$
2. $(A \land B) \rightarrow \sim A$ // $\sim A$
3. $A \rightarrow (A \land B)$ 1 Abs
4. $A \rightarrow \sim A$ 3,2 HS
5. $\sim A \lor \sim A$ 4 Impl
6. $\sim A$ 5 Taut

Absorption (Abs) is less commonly used than, say, MP. But here it sets up an HS with line 2. Some mistakenly believe that line 4 is contradictory. But lines 5 and 6 show that $A \rightarrow \sim A$ is equivalent to A, which is hardly a contradiction.

(18) 1. A
2. B   // $A \leftrightarrow B$
3. $A \land B$ 1,2 Conj
4. $(A \land B) \lor (\sim A \land \sim B)$ 3 Add
5. $A \leftrightarrow B$ 4 Equiv

Addition can be very useful, especially when you can determine that some version of what you want is a disjunction. The second version of Equiv is a disjunction. This is another example of finding a logical equivalent of the conclusion and then looking for rules that will connect the premises with this equivalent.

(19) 1. A→(B∧C)
   2. B→(C→D)   //A→D
   3. (B∧C)→D   2 Exp
   4. A→D   1,3 HS

We used Abs and Taut in (17) and used the second version of Equiv and Conj in (18). That leaves Exportation (Exp), which is of use here.

The fundamental principles of logic can be introduced to a reader who is willing to work through sets of relatively simple exercises. Although harder and more time-consuming problems would raise the reader's level of competence, it is the purpose of this book to provide a brief but thorough introduction. With few exceptions, the exercises in this book are beginning exercises. I make these remarks as an apology for the length of the next and last proof in this set of examples. This proof has been included, in part, because you only need follow it. Recall that proof-following is much easier than proof-constructing. The major reason for including the proof is that it illustrates nicely some thought processes which underlie much proof construction. Since I am concerned with these thought processes, the unfolding proof will be interrupted by commentary. As you follow along, notice the following questions recurring:

(a) What do I need?
(b) Where can I find what I need?
(c) What rule is required to help me obtain what I need?
(d) Does the rule demand that I find something else in order to use it?

(20) 1. A→(B∨C)
   2. C→(D∨E)
   3. F→~(G∧H)
   4. ((F∧A)∧I)→H
   5. E→G
   6. A→I
   7. F∧A
   8. (D→J)∧~J   //F∧B

Since the conclusion of this problem is a conjunction, we need to obtain an F from the premises and then a B. Once we do, we simply use Conj to form F∧B. Where can we find an F? Obviously, in line 7.

9. F   7 Simp

In a sense, the proof is half over. However, breaking out B may take a bit longer. Where can we find a B? The only B in the premises is in line 1. Unfortunately, this B is mixed up with an A and a C. We must break up line 1. Since line 1 is primarily an implication, we need a rule which breaks up implication statements. MP does this, but to use MP we also need, on a separate line, the antecedent of line 1. That is, we need an A. There is an A available in line 7.

10. A   7 Simp

Now we can use lines 1 and 10 to break B∨C out of line 1.

11. B∨C   1,10 MP

We still want B, which is still connected with C. We must eliminate that C. DS is the rule that breaks up disjunctions, and line 11 is a disjunction. DS tells us that we need a ~C to go with line 11, if we are to break out B, and also tells us that C must be moved to the left of the '∨' in line 11.

12. C∨B   11 Comm

Now where can we find a ~C? It would seem that ~C must somehow come from line 2. Line 2 is an implication. Which rule breaks up implication statements and yields the negation of the antecedent? The answer is MT (check the rule). To use MT on line 2, we need on a separate line the negation of the consequent of line 2, namely, ~(D∨E). ~(D∨E) is not evident among the premises. So let us look at another form of ~(D∨E). DeM tells us that ~(D∨E) is equivalent to ~D∧~E. This suggests that we might look for ~D and then for ~E. If we find them, we can put them together with Conj and use DeM to set up a use of MT on line 2. Where do we find a ~D? Line 8 is promising.

13. D→J   8 Simp
14. ~J   8 Simp
15. ~D   13,14 MT

Now we need ~E. There is an E on line 5. If we had a ~G, we could use it with line 5 (and MT) to obtain ~E. There is a G in line 3. Let us see what happens if we break up that line.

16. ~(G∧H)   3,9 MP
17. ~G∨~H   16 DeM
18. ~H∨~G   17 Comm
19. H→~G   18 Impl

Well, we've made some progress with line 3, but we still don't have a ~G. To get ~G from line 19 we need an H. There is an H sitting at the tail end of line 4. All we need is (F∧A)∧I and MP to break H out of line 4. We have F∧A in line 7 and we can get I from line 6.

20. I	6,10 MP
21. (F∧A)∧I	7,20 Conj
22. H	4,21 MP
23. ~G	19,22 MP

Now why did we want ~G? As I recall we needed it to get ~E from line 5.

24. ~E	5, 23 MT

And why did we want ~E? We wanted it to go with ~D (line 15) so that we could finally reach ~C. So let's do it.

25. ~D∧~E	15,24 Conj
26. ~(D∨E)	25 DeM
27. ~C	2,26 MT

We wanted ~C to obtain B from line 12.

28. B	12,27 DS

And we want B to go with F so we can get out of this proof.

29. F∧B	9,28 Conj

A proof of this length generally inhibits beginners. But it isn't too difficult if one asks the right questions and doesn't lose patience. The material needed is somewhere in the premises. Those premises have a certain form and only certain rules will work on certain forms. The rules tell you what else you need in order to use them on the lines in question. You cannot manufacture these other needs from nothing, but you can find them elsewhere in the premises.

We now turn to two important and powerful rules of inference not treated thus far.

Conditional Proof (CP)

I could try to be cute and tell a weird story that involves a use of conditional proof, but the first reaction of most people to CP is that the rule itself is weird—seemingly a principle of "anti-logic." Although this initial reaction is mistaken, I would not want to deprive you of an apparent encounter with "anti-logic." So I'll skip the story and go directly to CP. Recall that our rules can be viewed as instructions for generating formulas. Here, in English, are the instructions for CP:

(1) "Assume on *any* line you wish *any* formula you wish."

"Does this mean I can write a new line anywhere in a proof and this line can be whatever I wish it to be?"

"It does, provided that the line is well-formed. That is, you cannot write things like '∧A' (since '∧' must connect two statements) or 'A∨B~' (since '~' must apply to something)."

"But this is crazy. We'll be pulling things out of thin air."

"Be patient, there is more to the rule."

(2) Use the rules to generate *at least one* line after your assumption, either from the assumption line or from any lines available to you which precede the assumption line.

(3) When you reach a line you want, terminate CP by writing on the line after the line you want: the assumption line followed by a → followed by the line you wanted.

(4) There are two restrictions on the use of CP.

(a) Once you have reached the conditional conclusion at the end of the proof, all other lines in this use of CP are no longer available to you as the proof proceeds. That is, one use of conditional proof produces no more than the conditional line at the end of CP. Were it otherwise, this would be a weird rule. CP does no more than conclude that if one assumes X, then it is possible to use the rules to produce Y (i.e., X→Y). The remainder of the CP is simply a demonstration that the rules will indeed produce Y, if X is assumed.

(b) Since it is possible to use CP at any time in a proof, one can make an assumption on one line and then another assumption on the next line and yet another assumption on the next line indefinitely. One must terminate the last assumption first, the second to last assumption second, and so on. It is possible, however, to make an assumption, terminate it, and then later make another assumption and terminate it. That means it is possible to have consecutive conditional proofs. The restriction here concerns nested conditional proofs.

"All of this is a bit abstract. A few examples would help."

"OK, I'll start with a single use of conditional proof. For contrast, I'll also do the same problem without CP."

With CP

1. (A∨B)→C //A→C	
→ 2. A	
3. A∨B	2 Add
4. C	1,3 MP
5. A→C	2– 4 CP

Without CP

1. (A∨B)→C //A→C	
2. ~(A∨B)∨C	1 Impl
3. C∨~(A∨B)	2 Comm
4. C∨(~A∧~B)	3 DeM
5. (C∨~A)∧(C∨~B)	4 Dist
6. C∨~A	5 Simp
7. ~A∨C	6 Comm
8. A→C	7 Impl

"Note that the assumption is indicated by the arrow pointing at line 2. Note that the *scope* of the assumption is indicated by the extension of that arrow down past all of the lines used to reach the conditional conclusion. In this proof, line 5 says in effect that, given line 1, if you assume A you can get C. Lines 2 through 4 show that this is true. Finally, note that proofs using CP tend to be shorter that those which do not."

"But how do I know when to use CP?"

"First look for conditional conclusions. In the preceding problem, the conclusion is A→C. Thus, one assumes A and tries to reach C. If C is reached, CP automatically produces A→C. If you have a conditional conclusion, assume the antecedent and try to reach the consequent. You might come across a conclusion involving several implication signs."

```
   1. A→C   //A→(B→C)
→  2. A
 → 3. B
   4. C            1,2 MP
   5. B→C          3–4 CP
   6. A→(B→C)      2–5 CP
```

"The conclusion here is primarily an implication, with A implying the stuff in the parentheses. Thus, we assume A in line 2 with the intent of arriving at B→C. Since B→C is also an implication, why not assume B and try to get C? We did just this in line 3. As noted in the second restriction on CP, the assumption made in line 3 must be terminated before the one in line 2. It should be obvious that any conclusion which can be converted into an implication will also yield to conditional proof. Suppose, for example, the conclusion of the problem above had been ~A∨(B→C). We know by the rule of implication that ~A∨(B→C) is equivalent to A→(B→C). We could have used the proof above and added a line 7, namely, ~A∨(B→C) (6 Impl). Obviously, CP is a powerful rule, so powerful that it can be used to generate conclusions from no premises at all. Suppose someone asked you to prove A∨~A, but gave you no premises. With CP you could proceed as follows:"

```
→ 1. A
  2. A∨~A            1 Add
  3. A→(A∨~A)        1–2 CP
  4. ~A∨(A∨~A)       3 Impl
  5. (A∨~A)∨~A       4 Comm
  6. A∨(~A∨~A)       5 Assoc
  7. A∨~A            6 Taut
```

"You had A∨~A in line 2. Why didn't you just stop there?"

"Once you begin a CP you must finish it. And once you finish it you have no more than the conditional statement underneath the termination line. Lines 1 and 2 are no longer available to you once that line is drawn. Note that the rules we use make it impossible for an assumption in a conditional proof—where there are no premises prior to the assumption—to be true and any line derived from that assumption to be false.

The conditional statement at the end of such CPs will always be a tautology. Another very common use of CP occurs when one must prove an equivalence. An illustration follows:"

> 1. (A∨B)→(C∧D)
> 2. (C∨D)→(A∨B)   //A↔C
> → 3. A
> 4. A∨B   3 Add
> 5. C∧D   1,4 MP
> 6. C   5 Simp
> 7. A→C   3–6 CP
> → 8. C
> 9. C∨D   8 Add
> 10. A∧B   2,9 MP
> 11. A   10 Simp
> 12. C→A   8–11 CP
> 13. (A→C)∧(C→A)   7,12 Conj
> 14. A↔C   13 Equiv

"Any time you see a conclusion that is an equivalence, remember that p↔q is equivalent to (p→q)∧(q→p). Such proofs should be treated as two separate proofs. First assume p and try to get q. If you succeed, you'll have p→q. Then assume q and try to get p. That should give you q→p. Put those two together with Conj, use Equiv on the conjunction, and you're finished. The scheme for CP follows:

> → p
> .
> .
> .
> q
> p→q

"Recall that an assumption inside another must be terminated first and that lines within the scope of a conditional proof cannot be used once the conditional conclusion is reached. Now let's look at an important variant on conditional proof."

Indirect Proof (IP)

A direct proof consists of constructing a conclusion from information given. An indirect proof consists of assuming a certain conclusion to be false, discovering that this assumption leads to a contradiction, and reasoning that the assumption must be false. That is, given a conclusion (a conjecture or hypothesis) p, one assumes ~p. If one can generate an expression of the form q∧~q from this assumption, one concludes ~p is false (i.e., that p is true). Indirect proof is based on the Law of the Excluded Middle: Every proposition is either true or false, but not both and not neither. Thus, if ~p is false, p must be true. Since one could test a conclusion without a negation sign and discover it led to a contradiction, we'll use two formulations of IP:

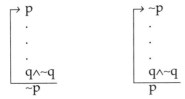

Indirect proof is a variant of conditional proof. In both cases one must make an assumption. In CP one can terminate the proof whenever he or she wishes. But in IP one must terminate with a line of the form q∧~q. We could replace every use of IP with a conditional proof as follows:

⌐→ p		Assume p.
·		
·		
q		Find q.
·		
·		
~q		Find ~q, which you must be able to do
q∨~p	Add	if IP will work here. Add ~p to q.
~p	DS	Use DS on q∨~p and ~q.
p→~p	CP	Finish the CP.
~p∨~p	Impl	Use Impl to set up a use of Taut.
~p	Taut	

We have the same conclusion IP would have given you. Note that IP was not used here and note that variables were used in the proof. The proof is perfectly general; it will work in every case where IP will work. Then, why use IP? Because it is shorter and a bit more intuitive than the CP version.

When IP is introduced into propositional logic, people usually ask when they should use it. The honest answer to this question begins with the observation that at this level of logic IP is often more trouble than it is worth. Proofs done with IP are usually longer than the corresponding direct proofs. The following proofs illustrate this point. Once the illustration is completed, the importance of IP will be revealed.

Without IP			**With IP**	
1. A→B			1. A→B	
2. B→C //A→C			2. B→C //A→C	
3. A→C	1,2 HS		3. ~(A→C)	
			4. A→C	1,2 HS
			5. (A→C)∧~(A→C)	4,3 Conj
			6. A→C	3–5 IP

One illustration does not prove that IP is usually more troublesome than a direct proof in propositional logic. The exercises in (C) at the end of this section should convince you. So why use IP? One finds the answer to this question by entering higher levels of logic, especially levels where it is possible to express number theory and mathematics beyond number theory. In number theory one encounters infinite domains, or finite domains so large that constructive procedures and searches are out of the question. For example, a mathematician named Vinogradoff proved that there exists a natural number V such that every successor of V is the sum of at most four primes. V, of course, is a finite number. Thus there is an infinite number of numbers each of which is the sum of at most four primes. It would be interesting to know which integer V is. But Vinogradoff did not know V's identity. How, then, did he know there is such a number? He knew by indirect proof. He supposed that a number satisfying V's conditions did not exist, derived a contradiction from this assumption, and concluded that V did exist.

There are more important uses of IP. The foundations of mathematical analysis (the foundations for the calculus) immerse one in the theory of infinite sets. A proof in these foundations, known as Cantor's diagonal procedure, is available to us only by indirect proof. It is difficult to keep infinity out of mathematics and so it is difficult to avoid indirect proof when doing mathematics. Someone once estimated that about fifty percent of contemporary mathematics would be unavailable to us if we were deprived of the IP rule. It is very important, therefore, for prospective mathematicians and computer scientists to be acquainted with indirect proof and to be proficient in its use. A few more illustrations of its use may help. You can practice IP on any problem.

(1) 1. P∨(Q∧R)
    2. ~R∨S
    3. S→~T //T→P
    4. ~(T→P)
    5. ~(~T∨P)   4 Impl
    6. ~~T∧~P   5 DeM
    7. ~~T   6 Simp
    8. ~P   7 Simp

9. ~S	3,7 MT
10. S∨~R	2 Comm
11.~R	10,9 DS
12. Q∧R	1,8 DS
13. R	12 Simp
14. R ∧~R	13,11 Conj
15. T→P	5–14 IP

Assume the negation of the conclusion, then break the conclusion up to obtain parts which will help in breaking up the premises. You are looking for a contradiction, one half of which will come from the premises and the other half of which comes from the negation of the conclusion. Note that if the argument is valid, the premises will produce the conclusion. By assuming the negation of the conclusion, one is assuming something inconsistent with the premises. The negation of the conclusion will produce a contradiction, but only if this assumption is used along with the premises.

(2)   1. ~(A∨~A)
      2.~A∧~~A   1 DeM
      3. A∨~A   1–2 IP

The task here is to prove A∨~A without being given any premises. Just assume the negation of what you wish to prove and proceed.

(3) 1. A∧B   //A↔B
     2.~(A↔B)
     3. (A∧B)∨(~A∧~B)   1 Add
     4. A↔B   3 Equiv
     5. (A↔B)∧~(A↔B)   4,2 Conj
     6. A↔B   2–5 IP

The conjuncts of the contradiction one finds in a use of IP may be complex, as they are in line 5 above. If one insisted on finding simple conjuncts, and there is no need to do this, (3) could be done as follows:

(3) 1. A∧B   //A↔B
     2. ~(A↔B)
     3. ~((A∧B)∨(~A∧~B))   2 Equiv
     4. ~(A∧B)∧~(~A∧~B)   3 Dem
     5. ~(A∧B)   4 Simp
     6. ~A∨~B   5 Dem
     7. A   1 Simp
     8. B   1 Simp
     9. ~~A   7 DN
     10. ~B   6,9 DS
     11. B∧~B   8,10 Conj
     12. A↔B   2–11 IP

By line 5, you have the parts of a contradiction (in lines 1 and 5), but if your heart is set on simple conjuncts you can get them.

Why would anyone elect (3)' over (3)? The most common reason for this is that someone, in searching for a solution, finds (3)', or some variation of it, first. Thus many proofs end up being longer than they need to be. This, as noted earlier, does not damage the validity of the proof. Validity is a binary condition; it does not come in degrees. Thus, a one-hundred-step proof that could have been done in four steps is just as correct as the four-step proof.

A second reason for proofs being longer than they need to be is that people sometimes make assumptions they need not make. For example, one might have taken on the proof above with the belief that the conjuncts of the contradiction in indirect proof must consist of a single letter and the negation of a single letter. This conviction is unwarranted, but in this case it does not prevent one from finishing the proof. At the outset of a proof, people often have the idea that a certain rule or rules must be used to finish or complete the proof. Sometimes this blinds them from seeing rules they really need. At other times it commits them to certain rules that will not take them to the conclusion. So try to keep an open mind by not inventing extra restrictions.

There is a difference between a proof with contradictory premises and an indirect proof. In a proof with contradictory premises, no assumptions need be made to arrive at the conclusion. You need not assume the conclusion is false in order to proceed. However, since any proof can be done using IP, a proof with contradictory premises can be done using IP, although that is not necessary. Compare the proofs below. They have the same contradictory premises, but only (5) uses IP.

(4)
1. P→Q
2. R→~Q
3. P∧R   //F
4. P   3 Simp
5. R   3 Simp
6. Q   1,4 MP
7. ~Q   2,5 MP
8. Q∨~F   6 Add
9. F   8,7 DS

(5)
1. P→Q
2. R→~Q
3. P∧R   //F
4. ~F
5. P   3 Simp
6. R   3 Simp
7. Q   1,5 MP
8. ~Q   2,6 MP
9. Q∧~Q   7,8 Conj
10. F   4–10 IP

Remember that one must conjoin Q and ~Q before IP can be completed. (See 5.)

We now have introduced all of the rules that will be used in constructing proofs in propositional logic. These rules will also be used when we move up to predicate logic. Do not sit down and memorize the rules. Simply do all of the exercises that follow. By the time you finish, you will know the rules. It is much better to learn rules by using them. When you learn by using, you begin to recognize structures, in the premises given, that suggest the appropriate rules.

Exercises

(A) The following exercises can be completed with just one step beyond the premises. All you need to do is find the single rule that permits that step. You won't need CP or IP for this set. Keep in mind that when constructing a proof you must write down a new line number, a new formula on that line, and the justification for the line to the right of the new formula. As usual, you will find answers for all exercises at the back of the book. Don't look at the answers too quickly. You cannot learn how to construct proofs if someone shows you how to do them. Imagine someone trying to teach you to play tennis by practicing for you and playing all your matches.

(1) 1. A→(B→C) //A→(~B∨C)

(2) 1. ~A∨(B→C) //A→(B→C)

(3) 1. A→(B→C) //(A∧B)→C

(4) 1. A→(B→C) //A→(A∧(B→C))

(5) 1. A→(B→C) //A→(B→~~C)

(6) 1. ~~(A→(B→C)) //A→(B→C)

(7) 1. A→(A∨A) //A→A

(8) 1. A→A // (A∧A)→A

(9) 1. ~A∨(B∧C) //(~A∨B)∧(~A∨C)

(10) 1. (~A∧B)∨(~A∧C) //~A∧(B∨C)

(11) 1. (A∨B)∨C //A∨(B∨C)

(12) 1. (A∨B)→(C→D)
     2. A∨B //C→D

(13) 1. (A∧B)∨~C
     2. ~(A∨B) //~C

(14) 1. (A→B)→~C
     2. ~C→~~A //(A→B)→~~A

(15) 1. A→(B→(C→D))
     2. ~(B→(C→D)) //~A

(16) 1. (A∧B)∨C //(B∧A)∨C

(17) 1. (A∧B)∨C //C∨(A∧B)

(18) 1. A∧B //(A∧B)∨C

(19) 1. A∧B //(A∧B)∨~(A∨B)

(20) 1. A→A //(A→A)∨(A→A)

(21) 1. ~A∨~A //~A

(22) 1. (A∨~B)∧(A∨~C) //A∨~C

(23) 1. ~(A∧B) //~A∨~B

(24) 1. ~A∧~B //~(A∨B)

(25) 1. ~A→~B //B→A

(26) 1. A∧(A∧A) //(A∧A)∧A

(27) 1. ~(A∧B)
     2. A∨B //(A∨B)∧~(A∧B)

(28) 1. ~(A∧B)
     2. A∨B //(A∨B)∨~(A∧B)

(29) 1. ~(A∧B)→~D
     2. ~~D //~~(A∧B)

(30) 1. ~(A∧B)→~D
     2. ~(A∧B) //~D

(B) Each exercise in the following set can be done in two steps. If you take more than two steps on a given problem, nothing is lost provided you used the rules correctly at each step and reached the correct conclusion. The exercises in (C) are slightly more interesting. Don't get impatient and jump to (C). This set won't take very long and it will continue to familiarize you with the rules. There is no need to use CP or IP in this set. Answers supplied for this set will use neither CP or IP.

(1) 1. A→(B→C) //~A∨(~B∨C)
(2) 1. ~B∨C // ~(B∧~C)
(3) 1. ~B∨C // (B→C)∨D
(4) 1. ~A∨(B∧C) //~A∨C
(5) 1. A→~A //~A
(6) 1. A∨(B∨C) //C∨(A∨B)
(7) 1. A∨B //~(~A∧~B)
(8) 1. (A∧B)∨(A∧C) //A
(9) 1. A→B //~A∨(A∧B)
(10) 1. (A↔B) //B→A
(11) 1. A→(B→C) //(B∧A)→C
(12) 1. ~(A∧B) //A→~B
(13) 1. A→B // B∨~A
(14) 1. A∨B //~A→B
(15) 1. A //(A∧A)∨(A∧A)
(16) 1. A↔B //(A∧B)∨~(A∨B)
(17) 1. ~A∨B //~B→~A
(18) 1. A //(A∧A)∨B
(19) 1. A∨(A∧B) //A∨A
(20) 1. ~((A→B)∨C) //~(A→B)
(21) 1. A∨B //~~A∨~~B
(22) 1. (~A∨B)∧(~A∨C) //A→(B∧C)
(23) 1. A→B //~A∨~~B
(24) 1. A→(A∧B) //(~A∨A)∧(~A∨B)
(25) 1. (B∧C)∧A //C∧(B∧A)
(26) 1. (A∧B)∧C //~(~(A∧B)∨~C)
(27) 1. ~A //A→B
(28) 1. ~(A∨B) //(~A∧~B)∨(A∧B)
(29) 1. C→D
  2. B→C
  3. A→B //A→D

(30) 1. (A∨B)∧(A∨C)
  2. ~A //B∧C
(31) 1. B→C
  2. ~A∨B //A→C
(32) 1. ~A∧B
  2. B→C //C
(33) 1. A∨B
  2. A∨C //A∨(B∧C)
(34) 1. A↔B
  2. ~(A∧B) //~A∧~B
(35) 1. A→~(B∧C)
  2. (~B∨~C)→D //A→D
(36) 1. A→B
  2. ~C→~B //A→C
(37) 1. A∨(B→C)
  2. ~A
  3. ~C //~B
(38) 1. B∨C
  2. ~C //B
(39) 1. ((A∧B)∧C)→D
  2. A∧(B∧C) //D
(40) 1. A→B
  2. B→~A //~A∨~A
(41) 1. A→B
  2. (A∧B)→C //A→C
(42) 1. A→B
  2. (B∧A)→C //A→(A→C)
(43) 1. (A∨(B∧C))→D
  2. A //D
(44) 1. A∨Z
  2. ~(A∨Z) //B

(C) Do each of the following problems twice, once with CP and again with IP. Answers for both versions are supplied in the back of the book.

(1) 1. (A∨B)→(C∧D) //B→D
(2) 1. (A∨B)→(C∧D) //(A∨B)→D
(3) 1. (A∨B)→(C∧D) //A→(C∧D)
(4) 1. (A∨B)→C
  2. C→(D∧E) //A→D
(5) 1. (A→B)∧(C→D)
  2. B→~D //~A∨~C
(6) 1. A→((B∧C)∨D)
  2. (B∧C)→~A //A→D
(7) 1. A∧(B∨C)
  2. ~C∨(~E∧F)
  3. E→~B //E→R
(8) 1. A→(B→C)
  2. ~C //~A∨~B
(9) 1. (A→B)∧(C→D)
  //(A∧C)→(B∧D)
(10) 1. A→D //(A→(B→(C→D)))
(11) 1. A∧B //A↔B

(12) 1. A↔(B∧C)
    2. (D∨E)→A //A∨~E
(13) 1. (A→B)∨(C∧D)
    2. A //~B→C
(14) 1. (A→B)∧(B→A)
    2. (B→C)∧(C→B) //A↔C

(15) 1. A→B
    2. C→D
    3. A∨C //B∨D
(16) 1. A→~A
    2. ~A→A //A↔~A

(D) Use any of the rules introduced thus far to solve the following problems. Use CP and IP as you see fit. Do not be discouraged if you do not find a way to prove some of these problems. You are just beginning. You should come away from this section of the book with a clear idea of what it is to construct a formal proof and with an understanding of standard rules of inference, especially conditional proof and indirect proof.

(1) 1. ~C
    2. B→C
    3. A∨B //A
(2) 1. A∨B
    2. B→C
    3. C→D //~A→D
(3) 1. ~A→B
    2. B→C
    3. C→D //A∨D
(4) 1. ~(A∧B)
    2. B∨C
    3. C→D //A→D
(5) 1. (A∨~B)→C
    2. C↔D
    3. A //D
(6) 1. A∧B
    2. (A∧B)→(C↔D)
    3. D∧~C //E
(7) 1. A→B
    2. B↔(C∧D)
    3. ~(A→D) //B→E
(8) 1. ~(A∧B)
    2. ~(C∧~B)
    3. ~(~C∧A) //~A
(9) 1. A→B
    2. B→(C→D)
    3. A→(B→C) //A→D
(10) 1. A∨~A
    2. A→(B∨~C)
    3. B→(D→E)
    4. ~E
    5. ~C→~F

6. F
7. ~A→G
8. ~G //~D
(11) 1. (A∨B)→(C∧D)
    2. (C∧E)→F
    3. (F∧G)→H //A→(E→(G→H)))
(12) 1. A→~B
    2. C→~D
    3. (A∨E)∧(E→C) //D→~(B∧F)
(13) 1. (A∨B)→(A∨~C)
    2. (C→A)→(A∧B)
    3. (B→D)∧(~E→~D) //~(A∧~E)
(14) 1. A∨((B∨C)→~D)
    2. ~(B→A)
    3. (D→A)→~E //~E
(15) 1. (~A→B)∧(B→C)
    2. B→~C
    3. B→(A→D) //B→D
(16) 1. (A∨B)∧(A∨C)
    2. ~B∨(~C∨D)
    3. (~D∨E)∧(~D∨F) //~(E∧F)→A
(17) 1. ~(A∧B)
    2. ~(A∧B)→(~A∧B)
    3. (A→B)→D //D
(18) 1. ~(A∨B)
    2. B∨(D∧E)
    3. D→~(A→C) //A
(19) 1. A∨(B∧C)
    2. ~C∨D
    3. D→~E //E→A
(20) 1. A∨(B∧C)
    2. B∧C

3. (D→~E)→~A

4. E→F

5. (G→H)∧(H→I)

6. (I→J)∧(J→K)

7. (~H∧~K)→L

8. (L→G)∧~K //F↔I

4

Evaluating Arguments in Predicate Logic

Symbolic logic has been disowned by many logicians on the plea that its interest is mathematical, and by many mathematicians on the plea that its interest is logical.

Alfred North Whitehead, *Universal Algebra* (1898)

Section 1
Showing Invalidity in Predicate Logic

You may recall from Chapter 1 that there are three kinds of statements in predicate logic: singular, particular, and universal. Singular statements do not need quantifiers because they name the individual in question. "Celia is smart" is a singular statement and can be symbolized as 'Sc.' "Someone is smart" is a particular (existential) statement, and requires a particular, or existential, quantifier. It can be symbolized as '$(\exists x)Sx$' (i.e., "There exists at least one x, such that x is smart."). Universal statements require universal quantifiers. For example, "Everyone is smart" might be symbolized as '$(\forall x)Sx$.'

There is a way to view any particular statement as a disjunction of singular statements. Suppose we have a list of all of the individuals in the universe and that this list is infinitely long, so we won't have to worry about whatever the number of individuals actually is. Let (a,b,c, . . .) represent this list, where 'a' is the name of the first individual on the list, 'b' the name of the second individual, and so on. Given this assumption, we may assert the following equivalence:

$(\exists x)Sx \leftrightarrow (Sa \lor Sb \lor Sc \ldots)$

That is, we may represent (∃x)Sx as an infinite disjunction that reads in English as "Either a has the property S, or b has S, or c has S, or . . ." This disjunction is true if at least one of the individuals on the list has the property S, and this is precisely what is asserted by (∃x)Sx. Complex existential statements receive exactly the same interpretation.

(∃x)(Ax∧Bx) ↔ ((Aa∧Ba)∨(Ab∧Bb)∨(Ac∧Bc)∨(Ad∧Bd)∨ . . .)
(∃x)(~Cx→~Dx) ↔ ((~Ca→~Da)∨(~Cb→~Db)∨(~Cc→~Dc)∨ . . .)

Whatever the expression covered by (∃x), we have the a-case followed by a '∨' followed by the b-case followed by '∨' and so forth. In effect, we have a means of dispensing with the existential quantifier. This "means," of course, usually isn't worth the complexity it brings with it.

A similar interpretation is available for universally quantified statements. For example, given our list of individuals we can assert the following equivalence:

(∀x)Sx ↔ (Sa∧Sb∧Sc∧ . . .)

"Everything has the property S" is quite reasonably translated as "The first individual, a, on the list has the property S, *and* so does b, and so does c, and so on ad infinitum." That is, each and every individual on the list has the property S, which is what (∀x)Sx claims. Complex universally quantified statements also turn out to be large conjunctions:

(∀x)(Ax→(Bx→Cx)) ↔ ((Aa→(Ba→Ca))∧(Ab→(Bb→Cb))∧ . . .)
(∀x)~(Ax∨Bx) ↔ (~(Aa∨Ba)∧~(Ab∨Bb)∧~(Ac∨Bc)∧ . . .)

Although it is by no means obvious at this point, the preceding interpretations of existential and universal statements are important for showing invalidity in predicate logic. To make things more obvious, consider two arguments, one of which is intuitively valid and one of which is intuitively invalid.

(1) 1. All cats are mammals.   (2) 1. Something is yellow.
     2. All mammals are animals.   2. Something is invisible.
     // All cats are animals.   // Something is yellow and
                                         invisible.

If we returned to propositional logic and symbolized these arguments, we would get:

(1) 1. C   (2) 1. Y
     2. M   2. I
     // A   // Y∧I

Two points about these symbolizations should be noted. First, in (1) line 1, we cannot write C→M, since 'cats' is not a statement nor is 'mammals.' Second, the symbolization of the conclusion of (2) should read "Something is yellow and something is square." Let us now translate both arguments into the notation of predicate logic. However, in the case of (2), let us translate "Something is yellow and invisible" as "There is at least one x such that x is both yellow and invisible."

(1) 1. $(\forall x)(Cx \rightarrow Mx)$
    2. $(\forall x)(Mx \rightarrow Ax)$
    // $(\forall x)(Cx \rightarrow Ax)$

(2) 1. $(\exists x)Yx$
    2. $(\exists x)Ix$
    // $(\exists x)(Yx \wedge Ix)$

To show that an argument is invalid, one must show that it is possible for the premises of the argument to be true while the conclusion is false. In Chapter 2, we did this by assigning truth values to the statements in question which made the premises true and the conclusion false. All we needed to do was find one case where such an assignment is possible, and we had demonstrated invalidity. Since lines 1 and 2 of (1) are statements, we can make them both true. Recall that we cannot assign a truth value to Cx, Mx, or Ax, since none of these are statements. We can also make the conclusion of (1) false. Thus as it stands, we can show that (1) is invalid. But clearly (1) is valid. Something is wrong with our method here.

Suppose, then, we violate our principle about assigning truth values only to statements, and permit Cx, Mx, and Ax to take on truth values. We ignore the quantifiers and reduce the argument to

(1) 1. $Cx \rightarrow Mx$
    2. $Mx \rightarrow Ax$
    // $Cx \rightarrow Ax$

To make the conclusion false, we make Cx true and Ax false. Since Ax is false, we must make Mx false to make line 2 true. When we do that, line 1 turns out false. And this is just what we expect from a valid argument: an argument in which it is impossible to make the conclusion false and still make all of the premises true. Have we found our method? Unfortunately, we have not. If we ignore the quantifiers in (2) above, we get

(2) 1. Yx
    2. Ix
    // $Yx \wedge Ix$

If anything in the conclusion is made false, a premise will be made false. So our method shows that this argument is valid. But the argument cannot be valid. If something is yellow and something else is invisible, it does not follow that there is one thing which is both yellow and invisible. We need a method for showing invalidity that will show that (2) is invalid, while preserving the validity of (1).

Understanding this method requires a careful review of the concept of validity: a valid argument is one where it is impossible for the premises to be true and the conclusion to be false at the same time. There is no possible world where the premises all turn out true and the conclusion turns out false. One shows an argument to be invalid by finding a world in which the premises are true and the conclusion is false. We are talking here about every possible world, not merely our physical universe. If you can even conceive of some world that is a counterexample to the argument, the argument is invalid.

Let us, then, consider a world in which exactly one individual exists. In this world, our list of individuals (a,b,c, . . .) is reduced to (a). That is, 'a' is the name of the only individual in this world. Now recall that every quantified statement has an interpretation in terms of disjunctions or conjunctions of individual cases. For example, (2) translates in the usual world as

(2) 1. (Ya∨Yb∨Yc . . .)
    2. (Ia∨Ib∨Ic . . .)
    // ((Ya∧Ia)∨(Yb∧Ib)∨(Yc∧Ic) . . .)

However, in the world consisting only of individual 'a,' (2) translates as

(2) 1. Ya
    2. Ia
    // Ya∧Ia

The something that is yellow (line 1) has to be 'a' because there are no other cases, such as b, c, or d. The something which is invisible would also have to be 'a.' Note that (2) *is* a valid argument in the possible world consisting of only one individual. One cannot make anything in the conclusion false without making a premise false.

An argument which is valid without qualification works in every possible world. To say that (2) is valid *in a universe of one individual* is not to say that (2) is valid. In fact, we might inquire as to whether (2) is valid in a universe of two individuals (call them 'a' and 'b'). If we translate (2) for a universe of two, we get

(2) 1. Ya∨Yb
    2. Ia∨Ib
    // (Ya∧Ia)∨(Yb∧Ib)

Now we have four statements to which we may assign truth values: Ya, Yb, Ia, Ib. If we make Ya and Ib false, the conclusion becomes false. If we make Yb true, line 1 becomes true. If we make Ia true, line 2 becomes true. These assignments show that (2) is invalid in a universe of two and, thus, simply invalid.

We have found a method for showing invalidity in predicate logic. The method amounts to seeking a counterexample against an argument. It consists of finding a universe of some number of individuals in which the premises can be made true, while the conclusion can be made false. The method is simple:

(a) Translate the argument for a universe of one individual.

(b) See if it is possible to show the argument is invalid under this translation. If it is, supply the truth values that show invalidity. If it is not, proceed to (c).

(c) Translate the argument for a universe of two individuals. This might be called "adding the b-case." For example, in a universe of one, $(\forall x)(Cx \rightarrow Dx)$ becomes $Ca \rightarrow Da$. If one moves to a universe of two, adding the b-case, one writes $(Ca \rightarrow Da) \wedge (Cb \rightarrow Db)$. Note that for universally quantified statements the b-case is "added" with an '$\wedge$.' Remember that a universally quantified statement is, essentially, a *conjunction* of cases. When adding the b-case for existentially quantified statements, such as $(\exists x)(Cx \wedge Dx)$, connect with a '$\vee$,' as in $(Ca \wedge Da) \vee (Cb \wedge Db)$. Having added the b-case, now try to show the argument invalid. If you can show invalidity, supply the appropriate truth values. If you cannot, go to a universe of three (a c-case). If three doesn't work, go to a universe of four (a d-case).

Could this process go on forever? No. If an argument in monadic-predicate logic is invalid, you will be able to show this without going beyond a universe of 2 raised to the number of predicates in the argument. Thus if there are three predicates (capital letters) in the argument, you will not have to go beyond a universe of eight. In this text, I won't force you beyond a universe of three. The principle of showing invalidity is important. You won't understand the principle any better by working in universes of seventeen or twenty-five. You may want to know, although I won't prove it here, that if an argument can be shown invalid in a universe of n, then it can be shown invalid in every universe greater than n. Let us turn to a few more examples:

(3) 1. $(\exists x)(Fx \wedge Gx)$ Start with a universe   1. $Fa \wedge Ga$
     2. $(\exists x)(Hx \wedge Ix)$ of one. The translation   2. $Ha \wedge Ia$
     3. $(\exists x)(Jx \wedge {\sim} Fx)$ is at the right.   3. $Ja \wedge {\sim} Fa$
     // $(\exists x)(Gx \wedge Ix)$ // $Ga \wedge Ia$

Fa, Ga, Ha, Ia, and Ja are all singular statements, that is, they are statements. So each of them can be assigned a truth value. If either Ga or Ia is made false in order to make the conclusion false, either the first or second premise will be made false. Thus the argument is valid in a universe of one. Another way of seeing that the argument is valid in a universe of one is to notice that you could use the rules to prove it. Simpify Ga from line 1, simplify Ia from line 2, and conjoin the results. This means we must move on to a universe of two. To do this we begin with the formulation to the right, above, and add a b-case.

		F	G	H	I	J
1.	$(Fa \wedge Ga) \vee (Fb \wedge Gb)$					
2.	$(Ha \wedge Ia) \vee (Hb \wedge Ib)$	a	F	F	T	T	T
3.	$(Ja \wedge {\sim} Fa) \vee (Jb \wedge {\sim} Fb)$	b	T	T	/	F	/
//	$(Ga \wedge Ia) \vee (Gb \wedge Ib)$						

The table of truth-value assignments to the right forces lines 1 through 3

to calculate to true and the conclusion to calculate to false. These assignments show that the argument is invalid. Line 2 had been made true by
assigning T to Ha and Ia. Ib was made false to make the second disjunct in
the conclusion false. Hb simply wasn't needed and, thus, a '/' was entered
in the table for Hb. Since Hb did not matter, entering a T or an F or a T/F for
Hb would be equally satisfactory. Jb received a '/' since it did no work in
this problem.

(4) 1. $(\exists x)(Ax \wedge Cx)$ First, go to a   1. $Aa \wedge Ca$
     2. $(\exists x)(\sim Ax \wedge Bx)$ universe of one.   2. $\sim Aa \wedge Ba$
     3. $(\exists x)(Bx \wedge Cx)$ 3. $Ba \wedge Ca$
     4. $(\exists x)(\sim Ax \wedge \sim Cx)$ 4. $\sim Aa \wedge \sim Ca$
     $// (\forall x)(Ax \rightarrow (Bx \rightarrow Cx))$ $// Aa \rightarrow (Ba \rightarrow Ca)$

Ca must be false if the conclusion is to be false. Making the conclusion
false automatically makes lines 1 and 3 false. Also note that since the premises contain a contradiction, anything can be validly derived from them.
And we move to a universe of two, and a b-case.

		A	B	C
1.	$(Aa \wedge Ca) \vee (Ab \wedge Cb)$			
2.	$(\sim Aa \wedge Ba) \vee (\sim Ab \wedge Bb)$	a	T	T	F
3.	$(Ba \wedge Ca) \vee (Bb \wedge Cb)$	b	T		T
4.	$(\sim Aa \wedge \sim Ca) \vee (\sim Ab \wedge \sim Cb)$				
$// (Aa \rightarrow (Ba \rightarrow Ca)) \wedge (Ab \rightarrow (Bb \rightarrow Cb))$				

It is necessary to make Aa and Ba true and Ca false, or to do the same in the
b-case, in order to make the conclusion false. If Ca is false, then both Ab and
Cb will have to be true if line 1 is to be true. But if Cb is true, then ~Cb in
line 4 will be false. And since Aa was made true, ~Aa in line 4 will be false.
Making the conclusion and line 1 true forces line 4 to be false. This argument is valid in a universe of two, and we must proceed to a universe of
three, a c-case.

		A	B	C
1.	$(Aa \wedge Ca) \vee (Ab \wedge Cb) \vee (Ac \wedge Cc)$			
2.	$(\sim Aa \wedge Ba) \vee (\sim Ab \wedge Bb) \vee (\sim Ac \wedge Bc)$	a	T	T	F
3.	$(Ba \wedge Ca) \vee (Bb \wedge Cb) \vee (Bc \wedge Cc)$	b	T	T	T
4.	$(\sim Aa \wedge \sim Ca) \vee (\sim Ab \wedge \sim Cb) \vee (\sim Ac \wedge \sim Cc)$	c	F	T	F
$// (Aa \rightarrow (Ba \rightarrow Ca)) \wedge (Ab \rightarrow (Bb \rightarrow Cb)) \wedge (Ac \rightarrow (Bc \rightarrow Cc))$				

The a-case assignments in the table do nothing more than guarantee that
the conclusion will be false. Note that the conclusion is a conjunction. If the
a-case is false, the entire conjunction will be false. This, of course, would
hold if either the b- or c-cases were made false. That is, we need a T,T,F in
the table and it does not matter on which line this occurs. The assignments
in the b-case make lines 1 and 3 true. Each of these lines is a disjunction and
we need only make one of the disjuncts on each line true to make the entire
line true. The assignments in the c-case make lines 2 and 4 true. The table

for a universe of three forces four true premises and a false conclusion. The argument is invalid.

Remember when moving to the b-case or the c-case that if the orginal statement had an existential quantifier, (∃x), the new cases are connected with a '∨.' If the quantifier is universal, (∀x), as it is in the conclusion of (4), the new cases are connected with a '∧.'

As with this technique in propositional logic, there may be more than one combination of truth values which show invalidity. Any one of these combinations, as long as it forces a false conclusion and true premises, is correct. There is no easy way to decide in advance which universe will do the job. For example, there is no general rule that tells you when you should skip universes one and two and go directly to three. So begin with a universe of one and proceed. As you gain experience, you may recognize cases where you can skip to a higher universe.

Exercises

Show each of the following arguments to be invalid by finding a universe in which the premises can be made true while the conclusion is made false. Your answer in each case will be a table of truth-value assignments.

(1) 1. (∃x)Ax
     // (∀x)Ax
(2) 1. (∃x)(Ax∧Bx)
     // (∀x)(Ax∧Bx)
(3) 1. Aa
     // (∃x)Bx
(4) 1. (∃x)Ax
     // Aa
(5) 1. (∀x)(Ax→Bx)
     2. (∀x)(Bx→Ax)
     // (∀x)Ax
(6) 1. (∀x)((Ax∨Bx)→Cx)
     2. (∃x)(Cx→Dx)
     3. (∃x)(Dx∧Ax)
     // (∀x)Cx
(7) 1. (∀x)(Ax∨Bx)
     2. (∀x)(Bx→Cx)
     3. (∃x)(Cx→Dx)
     // (∃x)(~Cx∧Dx)
(8) 1. (∀x)((Ax∨Bx)→Cx)
     2. (∀x)(Cx→Dx)
     3. (∃x)(Dx∧Ex)
     // (∃x)(Ax∧Dx)

(9) 1. (∀x)(Ax→Bx)
     2. (∀x)(Bx→Cx)
     3. (∀x)(Cx→Dx)
     4. (∀x)(Dx→Ex)
     // (∃x)(Ax∧Ex)
(10) 1. (∃x)Ax
     2. (∃x)Bx
     3. (∃x)Cx
     4. (∃x)Dx
     // (∃x)((Ax∧Bx)∧Cx)
(11) 1. (∀x)(Ax∨Bx)
     // (∃x)(Ax→Bx)
(12) 1. (∀x)(Ax→Bx)
     // (∃x)(Ax∧Bx)
(13) 1. Aa
     // (∀x)Ax
(14) 1. Aa∧(∃x)Bx
     // (∃x)(Ax∧Bx)
(15) 1. (∃x)(Cx∧Dx)
     2. (∃x)(Dx∧~Cx)
     // (∃x)(~Cx∧Dx)
(16) 1. (∀x)(Ax→Bx)
     2. (∃x)Ax

3. (∃*x*)Cx
   // (∃*x*)(Bx∧Cx)
(17) 1. (∃*x*)Ax
   2. (∃*x*)~Ax
   3. (∃*x*)Cx
   // (∃*x*)Dx
(18) 1. (∀*x*)(Ax→Bx)
   2. (∀*x*)(Ax→(Bx→Cx))
   3. (∃*x*)(Cx→Ax)
   // (∀*x*)(Ax↔Cx)

(19) 1. (∀*x*)(Ax↔Bx)
   2. (∀*x*)(Bx↔Cx)
   3. (∀*x*)(Cx↔Dx)
   4. (∀*x*)(Dx↔Ex)
   // (∀*x*)(Ax∨Ex)
(20) 1. (∃*x*)(Ax∧(Bx∧Cx))
   2. (∃*x*)(~Ax∧~Bx)
   3. (∀*x*)(Ax↔Dx)
   4. (∀*x*)(Dx→Ex)
   // (∀*x*)(Ax→Bx)

Section 2
Proving Arguments Valid
in Monadic Predicate Logic

Let us begin with an example of an argument that is at least intuitively valid:

(1) 1. (∀*x*)(Ax→Bx)
   2. (∀*x*)(Bx→Cx) // (∀*x*)(Ax→Cx)

In English, this argument says that if all A's are B's and all B's are C's, then surely all A's are C's. However, if we translate this argument into the notation of propositional logic, letting A stand for line 1, B for line 2, and C for the conclusion, we can show the argument to be invalid by making A and B true and C false. In short, we must remain in predicate logic if we are to prove that this argument is valid. We recognize this argument as valid because of its internal structure—because of the relations among the predicates Ax, Bx, and Cx. We might consider proving this argument valid by ignoring the quantifiers and simply using the rules on

1. Ax→Bx
2. Bx→Cx // Ax→Cx

It looks as though a proof is available by using HS on lines 1 and 2. However, there are two reasons why we cannot do this. First, Ax, Bx, and Cx are not statements. Line 1, as it stands, translates:

If ____ has the property A, then ____ has the property B.

We cannot assign this expression a truth value, since we are not told how to fill in the blanks. The expression is not singular, since no one is named. It is not particular, since it is not about something. And it is not universal, since it is not about everything. We just aren't told what it is about. Admittedly we came up with this expression by ignoring the universal quantifier in line 1 of (1). But that is the point. Once the quantifier is ignored, the expression ceases to be a statement. Our rules of inference are defined for statements. They do not apply to incomplete expressions, such as Ax. Thus, we cannot use these rules, such as HS, on Ax→Bx and Bx→Cx.

A second reason for not ignoring quantifiers is that it would permit us to prove arguments that are invalid. For example,

(2) 1. (∃x)(Ax∧Bx)
     2. (∃x)(Bx∧Cx) //(∀x)(Ax∧Cx)

If we ignore the quantifiers in (2), we can simplify Ax from line 1, Cx from line 2, and use Conj to reach the conclusion. If this could count as a proof of (2), we would have proved that if something has A and B, and something has B and C, then everything has A and C. For example, if some aardvarks are beautiful, and some beautiful things are cats, then everything is an aardvark and a cat. So we cannot simply ignore the quantifiers. We cannot operate on the internal parts of a quantified statement as though the quantifier isn't there.

The preceding observations suggest that we must satisfy two conditions when constructing proofs in predicate logic: (a) The quantifiers supply us with information which we must preserve as we proceed through a proof. (b) We cannot work on the internal structure of a statement while the quantifier is attached. These two conditions tell us that we need a way of stripping quantifiers from formulas while preserving the information given in the quantifier. There is nothing mysterious about what this information is: "(∃x)" tells us we are dealing with at least one particular thing (perhaps exactly one particular thing) and "(∀x)" says that we are dealing with each and every individual in the universe.

The account given here of stripping quantifiers, while preserving the information in them, is based on the one given by Irving M. Copi in his *Introduction to Logic* (New York: Macmillan, 1961). This account trades on the difference between a variable and a dummy name.

The x in Ax is a variable. It is a blank which can be filled by an individual from some domain of individuals. The 'a' in Aa is not a variable, but a proper name, such as Amy. Now suppose you were told someone is nine feet tall, but not who that someone is. That is, you are told (∃x)Nx. You presume this person has a name and since you don't know this name, you make one up. Lacking imagination this day, the best you can do is 'x.' X, in this case, is not a variable, it is a dummy name.

Suppose you are also told that everything has a mass (i.e., (∀x)Mx). You find it difficult to imagine "everything" and so you arbitrarily pick some individual, call it x, and let the fact that this x has a mass stand for the claim that everything has a mass. You use x having a mass to represent everything having a mass. This is not unreasonable, since x was arbitrarily selected. Anything might have been selected in its place. This randomly selected x is an individual, one you have named 'x' because you neither know nor care what its real name is. Thus this random x is not a variable, it is a dummy name.

The account of the quantifier rules presented in the following pages involves dummy names, not variables. However, it is common practice to refer to these names as variables. This practice is due in part to a view of logic that has not been adopted in this book. Logic may be seen as a collection of well-defined games that involve notation manipulation. A game need not be about anything and notation in a game need not name anything. The difference between variables and proper names is preserved, on this alternate view, as the difference between a variable and a constant. The difference between a variable and a dummy name is preserved by the rules which restrict quantifier operations. I realize that the remarks in this paragraph are not likely to make much sense at this stage of the presentation. They are included here only to indicate a problem I face in the presentation. A careful use of language, which would involve repeated uses of the expression *dummy name,* will not read well and will not conform to common usage among logicians. Common usage permits the term *variable* to be used in a variety of situations, since one familiar with those situations will have little trouble in understanding how the meaning of the term changes from one context to the next. To resolve this problem, I will use the expression *dummy name* when introducing a rule. After that, I will revert to calling subscripts that are not proper names *variables* and, at times in an effort to sidestep the issue, simply *subscripts.*

In Chapter 1 you were introduced to the difference between bound and free variables. Bound variables are those falling within the scope of a quantifier. Free variables do not fall within the scope of a quantifier. The variable x at A in $(\forall x)Ax$ is bound. The x at A in Ax is free. In $(\exists x)Ax \wedge Bx$, the x at A is bound, but the x at B is free. In $(\exists x)(Ax \wedge Bx)$ the occurrences of x at both A and B are bound.

Strictly speaking, formulas with free variables are incomplete and cannot have truth values. [For the moment, permit me to call such free variables "strictly speaking free variables," since I will end up calling any unquantified formula that does not have subscripts representing proper names a formula with free variables.] Our truth preserving rules from Chapter 3 cannot be used on formulas with strictly speaking free variables (unless, of course, we revert to the game-playing view of logic). We need a way of stripping away quantifiers and not producing formulas with strictly speaking free variables in the process. This can be done by stripping away a quantifier and implicitly treating the remaining variables as if they were terms for individuals in singular statements.

For example, suppose we have $(\exists x)Ax$ and want to remove the $(\exists x)$. We write Ax, but we no longer treat Ax as meaning "____ has the property A." Instead, we say that x is the *dummy name* for whatever it is that makes $(\exists x)Ax$ true. Recall that

$(\exists x)Ax \leftrightarrow (Aa \lor Ab \lor Ac \lor \ldots)$

For $(\exists x)Ax$ to be true, at least one of the disjuncts to the right of the $\leftrightarrow$ sign above must be true. Our problem is that we don't know which one it is; we have been told only that *something* has the property A. So when stripping $(\exists x)$ from $(\exists x)Ax$ we say that x in the remaining Ax is the name of that something that makes $(\exists x)Ax$ true. We don't know what its real name is, so we'll call it 'x.'

How are we to know that x is a dummy name and not a strictly speaking free variable? We know because this x was "introduced" in the operation of stripping away $(\exists x)$ from $(\exists x)Ax$. There is nothing arbitrary in introducing this x, since it is our name for whatever it is that makes $(\exists x)Ax$ true. That whatever may be exactly one individual.

A different kind of "introduction" can go on when we strip away $(\forall x)$ from $(\forall x)Ax$. As noted

$(\forall x)Ax \leftrightarrow (Aa \land Ab \land Ac \land \ldots)$

Each and every individual must have the property A for $(\forall x)Ax$ to be true. If we wanted to strip away $(\forall x)$ from $(\forall x)Ax$ and preserve the universality of the claim, we could *randomly* select one of the conjuncts above and call it 'x.' Imagine having a giant bag of individuals each one of which is yellow. You close your eyes, reach into the bag, grab an individual, pull it out, and name it 'x.' Of course x is yellow. But it is not yellow because you made some special or biased choice. It is yellow because all the individuals in the bag are yellow. Given the way you selected this individual, your choice could easily have been any other individual in the bag. You might say that this selection stands for all other possible selections. By randomly selecting this case, you let it stand for "All individuals in the bag are yellow." And so it is with x randomly selected from $(\forall x)Ax$ (i.e., from $(Aa \land Ab \land Ac \land \ldots)$). You don't care which one it is, since any other choice will do just as well. A randomly selected case from a universally quantified claim preserves generality.

Ax produced by stripping away $(\exists x)$ from $(\exists x)Ax$ means something quite different than Ax produced by a random selection from $(\forall x)Ax$. The selection of x in the existential case means: I am going to call whatever it is that makes $(\exists x)Ax$ true 'x.' The selection of x in the universal case means: I am going to call the individual randomly selected from $(\forall x)Ax$ 'x.'

When dealing with a universally quantified statement one has options other than random selections. Since the $(\forall x)$ in $(\forall x)Ax$ tells us that every individual in the universe has the property A, we can select any one of these individuals. We can strip away the universal quantifier and leave Aa or Ab or whatever. We can choose any proper name we wish as a subscript, since a universal claim is true for all individuals.

We can make one other kind of choice from a universal claim. This involves matching a choice made when stripping away an existential quantifier. Consider the following proof:

1. $(\exists x)Ax$
2. $(\forall x)(Ax \rightarrow Bx)$ $//(\exists x)Bx$
3. Ax (Obtained from line 1 by removing $(\exists x)$ and letting x in line 3 stand for whatever individual made line 1 true.)
4. $Ax \rightarrow Bx$ (Obtained from line 2 by choosing the same x that was chosen in line 3. The occurrences of x in lines 3 and 4 stand for the same individual.)
5. Bx 4,3 MP
6. $(\exists x)Bx$ (If some individual x has the property B (line 5), then something has B (line 6).)

When getting rid of $(\exists x)$ you can make only one kind of selection, namely, the particular x that makes the statement true. However, when getting rid of $(\forall x)$, you have three possible choices. You can randomly select an x, preserving the universality of the orginal claim, or you can select any proper name you wish, or you can match an x introduced in an earlier step where an $(\exists x)$ was stripped away. Once the quantifiers have been stripped, you may proceed using the rules introduced in Chapter 3.

Since we must strip away quantifiers while preserving the information they contain in order to use the propositional rules, we ought to have precisely formulated rules for the stripping operation. Since most conclusions in predicate logic are quantified statements, we'll also need rules for putting quantifiers back. There are only two quantifiers. So, we need only four such rules, two for stripping and two for putting back.

Quantifier Rules

Existential instantiation (EI): This is the rule for stripping away an existential quantifier. There are restrictions on its use that prevent us from making errors. In the formulation below, Fx stands for any formula whatsoever in which there are occurrences of x.

    $(\exists x)Fx$
    $// Fx$ (I'll call it 'x'.)
    $// Fy$ (Or I'll call it 'y', and of course I could give it any other dummy name, such as 'z' or 'w.'

If we are going to use all these letters for dummy names, we'll need a convention for identifying proper names. The convention for this book, which is peculiar to this book, is that lower-case letters *a* through *s* may stand for proper names and lower case letters *t* through *z* may stand for dummy names and variables. So, for example, Bm might stand for "Mary is bad," while By stands for "I'm calling whatever made $(\exists x)$Bx true 'y.'"

Restriction 1: When using EI, you cannot choose a proper name for a subscript. $(\exists x)$Bx tells you that someone is bad, but it does not tell you who that someone is. Thus you cannot move from $(\exists x)$Bx to, say, Bc, where c stands for Charlie. If you did, you'd be claiming to know that Charlie is bad based solely on the information that someone is bad. This simply doesn't follow.

Restriction 2: When using EI, you may not choose a subscript that is already "free" (unquantified) in the proof. If we ignored this restriction, we could execute the following proof:

1. $(\exists x)$Sx
2. $(\exists x)$Cx //$(\exists x)$(Sx∧Cx)
3. Sx   1 EI
4. Cx   2 EI
5. Sx∧Cx   4,5 Conj
6. $(\exists x)$(Sx∧Cx)   5 EG (which hasn't been introduced yet)

Suppose $(\exists x)$Sx stands for "Something is a square" and $(\exists x)$Cx for "Something is a circle." In line 3 above, we decided to call the square 'x'. In line 4, we decided to call the circle 'x.' That is, in line 4 we claimed to know that the circle is identically the same individual that is square. Did we know this from the information in lines 1 and 2? Obviously we did not. Lines 1 and 2 could refer to entirely different individuals. In the case of circles and squares, they must refer to different individuals. So do not allow the occurrence of x in both lines 1 and 2 to mislead you into believing that these lines must be about the same something. The second restriction on EI is designed to prevent mistakes arising from such misconceptions. Each time you use EI in a proof you must choose a different subscript. You must assume that this new something may be different from other somethings talked about in the proof.

Restriction 2 on EI also covers the following cases:

1. $(\forall x)$(Ax→Bx)
2. $(\exists x)$Ax //$(\exists x)$Bx
3. Ax→Bx   1 UI (a rule yet to be introduced)
4. Ax   2 EI (This use of EI violates Restriction 2,
                   since x occurs free in line 3.)

The problem we face is easily resolved by doing EI first:

3. Ax   2 EI (There are no free occurrences of x prior to line 3.)
4. Ax→Bx   1 UI
5. Bx   4,3 MP
6. $(\exists x)$Bx   5 EG

The only way, other than the removal of a quantifier, that a free variable might be introduced is through an assumption for either conditional proof or indirect proof:

1. $(\forall x)((Ax \lor Bx) \rightarrow Cx)$
2. $(\exists x)(Cx \rightarrow Dx) \; // (\exists x)(Ax \rightarrow Dx)$
3. Ax
4. $Cx \rightarrow Dx$ 2 EI (This violates the second restriction, since x is free in line 3.)

Once again, we can remove the difficulty by doing EI first:

3. $Cx \rightarrow Dx$ 2 EI
4. Ax
5. $(Ax \lor Bx) \rightarrow Cx$ 1 UI
6. $Ax \lor Bx$ 4 Add
7. $\underline{Cx}$ 5,6 MP
8. $Ax \rightarrow Cx$ 4-7 CP
9. $Ax \rightarrow Dx$ 3,8 HS
10. $(\exists x)(Ax \rightarrow Dx)$ 9 EG

Suppose we had several existentially quantified statements in a proof and we had to use all of them to complete the proof:

1. $(\forall x)(Ax \rightarrow Bx)$
2. $(\exists x)Ax$
3. $(\exists x)\sim Bx$
4. $(\exists x)(Ax \land Cx)$ $//(\exists x)\sim Ax \land ((\exists x)Bx \land (\exists x)(Bx \land Cx))$
5. Ax   2 EI   (EI first, but it doesn't matter which one)
6. $\sim By$ 3 EI   (You must choose a different subscript.)
7. $Az \land Cz$ 4 EI   (and yet another subscript that is not free earlier in the proof)
8. $Ax \rightarrow Bx$ 1 UI   (Since $(\forall x)$ covers all possible subscripts, you can choose x as a subscript.)
9. $Ay \rightarrow By$ 1 UI   (And you can choose y to go with $\sim By$ in line 6.)
10. $Az \rightarrow Bz$ 1 UI   (All possible subscripts include z, to go with $Az \land Cz$ in line 7.)
11. Bx   8,5 MP
12. $(\exists x)Bx$ 11 EG
13. $\sim Ay$ 9,6 MT
14. $(\exists x)\sim Ax$ 13 EG   (You can go from y in 13 to a quantified x in 14, since 14 says "Something doesn't have A." Line 14 would say the same thing no matter what subscript is used. $(Ey)\sim Ay$ and $(\exists x)\sim Ax$ mean the same thing. However, Ax does not mean what

Ay means, since x and y may be different individuals.)

15. Az	7 Simp	
16. Cz	7 Simp	
17. Bz	10,15 MP	
18. Bz∧Cz	17,18 Conj	
19. (∃x)(Bx∧Cx)		18 EI
20. (∃x)Bx∧(∃x)(Bx∧Cx)		12,19 Conj
21. (∃x)~Ax∧((∃x)Bx∧(∃x)(Bx∧Cx))		14,20 Conj

Restriction 3: EI must be used on an entire line. The (∃x) that is being removed must be the lead symbol on the line and its scope must include
everything else on the line. Thus the following moves are illegal:

| 1. (∃x)Ax∨(∀x)Bx | | |
| 2. Ax∨(∀x)Bx | 1 EI | (The scope of (∃x) covers the x at A but not the remainder of the line.) |

| 1. (∀x)Ax∧(∃x)Bx | | |
| 2. (∀x)Ax∧Bx | 1 EI | (Again, (∃x) does cover all of line 1.) |

One could resolve the problem faced in the second illustration by simplifying (∃x)Bx from line 1 and then using EI. This won't work, of course, with
the first illustration. You cannot simplify from an or-statement.

| 1. ~(∃x)Ax | | |
| 2. ~Ax | 1 EI | ((∃x) does not cover the lead '~.') |

Restriction 4: When using EI, all of the occurrences of x (or y or z or
whatever subscript is in question) covered by the quantifier must be treated
in the same way. The following are violations of this restriction:

| 1. (∃x)(Ax∧Bx) | |
| 2. Ax∧By | 1 EI |

| 1. (∃x)(Ax∧Bx) | |
| 2. Ay∧Bz | 1 EI |

As noted earlier, it is permissible to change subscripts when using EI. Just
change all occurrences of the subscript in the same way. The following is
legal:

| 1. (∃x)(Ax∧Bx) | |
| 2. Ay∧By | |

The restrictions on EI make it a more complex rule than, say, MP. Some
people are irritated with this increase in complexity, and ignore the restrictions. Thus they make logical errors. Since we are introducing here only
four quantifier rules, the restrictions should not be too much to learn. Here
in summary is EI:

(∃x)Fx

//x   or any other subscript you choose provided that

F   (1) the subscript is not a proper name,

                     (2) the subscript is not free earlier in the proof

                          (in which case you must choose a different one),

                     (3) (∃x) covers the entire line, and

                     (4) all occurrences of x are treated in the same way.

Universal instantiation (UI): This is the rule for stripping away a universal quantifier. The only restrictions on its use are that (∀x) must cover the entire line and all occurrences of x covered by (∀x) must be treated in the same way. UI offers several options:

Option 1.   (∀x)Fx

           //Fx   where x is the dummy name of a random selection.

This option permits you to return to a universally quantified statement at the end of proof, as follows:

1. (∀x)(Ax→Bx)
2. (∀x)(Bx→Cx)   //(∀x)(Ax→Cx)
3. Ax→Bx   1 UI   (a randomly selected x)
4. Bx→Cx   2 UI   (the same x as in line 3)
5. Ax→Cx   3,4 MP
6. (∀x)(Ax→Cx)   5 UG   (UG is still to be introduced)

Option 2.   (∀x)Fx

           //Fx   where x is was introduced by a use of EI earlier

                  in the proof.

This option leads to a restriction, to be picked up by the universal generalization (UG) rule, from returning to a universally quantified statement. When you choose x in this case, you are choosing the individual that made the existential claim true. You are choosing to talk about a special case.

1. (∃x)Ax
2. (∀x)(Ax→Bx)   //(∃x)Bx
3. Ax   1 EI   (remember, EI first)
4. Ax→Bx   2 UI   (This is not a random selection; it is

                                      the individual referred to in line 3.)
5. Bx   4,3 MP
6. (∃x)Bx   5 EG   (EG is coming.)

Option 3.   (∀x)Fx

           //Fa   or b or c or any other individual for which you

                  have the proper name.

Since (∀x) covers all cases, it covers any particular case. Obviously you won't be able to use this UI option and return to a universally quantified conclusion. What is true for Ann, if c stands for Ann, is not necessarily true for everything.

1. Ac
2. $(\forall x)(Ax \rightarrow Bx)$ //Bc
3. Ac→Bc   2 UI
4. Bc   3,1 MP

You might note that UI can be used repeatedly on one line. An example of this occurred in the long proof illustrating the second restriction on EI.
   In summary the UI rule is as follows:

$(\forall x)Fx$
// Fx   where x is randomly selected, or
// Fx   where x was selected by a use of EI, or
// Fa   where a is any proper name. $(\forall x)$ must cover the entire line and all occurrences of x must be treated alike.

Special note: UI can be used as many times as you wish on the same universal statement. Using UI is like simplifying from a conjunction with an infinite number of conjuncts.
   Existential generalization (EG): This is the rule for putting back, or introducing, existential quantifiers. When you use EG you must quantify an entire line.

Fx or Fa
//$(\exists x)Fx$

It does not matter whether the subscript came from a random selection using UI, or from a particular case using EI, or whether it is a proper name. If *any* case has a certain property, then something has that property.
   Restriction: Only one kind of subscript can be quantified at a time. The following are violations of this restriction:

1. Ac∧Be
2. $(\exists x)(Ax \wedge Bx)$ 1 EG

If we permitted this, we would be saying that because something named c and something else named e had the property B, that some one thing had the properties A and B. We could, however, write:

2. $(\exists x)(Ax \wedge Be)$ 1 EG

The entire line has been quantified, and reads "Either something has the property A and e has B." This does follow from line 1, which reads "c has A and e has B."
   The restriction applies equally to x's and y's, whatever their source. The following would be in error:

1. Ax∧By
2. $(\exists x)(Ax \wedge Bx)$ 1 EG

Line 1 tells us that some x has A and that something else, y, has B. It does not follow that there is one thing that has both A and B, as line 2 claims it does.

In summary, EG is as follows:

Fx or Fa
$//(\exists x)Fx$

That is, the subscript does not matter provided one kind of subscript is quantified with one use of EG.

Universal generalization (UG): This rule introduces universal quantifiers. Since we wish to avoid reaching a universal conclusion from premises about particular cases, there are restrictions on the use of UG.

Fx
$//(\forall x)Fx$

Restriction 1: UG cannot be used on a singular statement, such as Ac. From the fact that some individual named 'c' has a certain property it does not follow that everything has that property. For example, if Chan is angry, it doesn't follow that everything is angry.

Restriction 2: UG cannot be used on a subscript produced by a use of EI. The following proof is in error:

1. $(\exists x)Dx$
2. Dx   1 EI   (a legal move)
3. $(\forall x)Dx$ 2 UI   (This is an illegal move. If we permitted it, we would have to allow that if someone is drunk, it logically follows that everyone is drunk.)

Given the length of some proofs, it is easy to lose track of how certain subscripts were introduced. There are only three ways in which free variables (subscripts without quantifiers) are introduced: by a use of EI, by a use of UI, or via an assumption. When you use UG, you must quantify on exactly one variable. You must check to see when that variable first occurred unbound by a quantifier. If this occurrence came from a use of EI, you cannot use UG on that variable. This restriction has no exceptions, not even the following:

1. $(\exists x)\sim Ax$
2. $(\forall x)(Ax \rightarrow Bx)$
3. $(\forall x)(Bx \rightarrow Cx)$ $//(\forall x)(Ax \rightarrow Cx)$
4. $\sim Ax$ 1 EI
5. $Ax \rightarrow Bx$ 2 UI
6. $Bx \rightarrow Cx$ 3 UI
7. $Ax \rightarrow Cx$ 5,6 HS
8. $(\forall x)(Ax \rightarrow Cx)$ 7 UG   (error)

Someone might try to argue that line 4 was not used in reaching the conclusion and, therefore, that the argument is valid. On the contrary, line 4 was used in reaching the conclusion. In line 4 the individual that does not have the property A, the individual that makes line 1 true, was designated as 'x.' The same individual was introduced in lines 5 and 6 by the selection of x as a subscript. Lines 5 and 6 are about a special case. And the use of UG in line 8 amounts to saying that because something is true for the special case in line 1 it is true for all cases. Reasoning from "some" to "all" is mistaken. There are two ways to avoid the difficulty in the example above. Either ignore line 1, so that there is no EI in line 4, or use a different subscript, such as y, in lines 5 and 6.

Restriction 3: You cannot use UG on a variable that is free in an assumption if you are still within the scope of that assumption. Don't do anything like the following:

→ 1.	Fx		
2.	(∀x)Fx	1 UG	(error)
3.	Fx→(∀x)Fx	1–2 CP	

Just because some individual x has the property F, it does not follow that all individuals have the property F. In contrast, the following proof is perfectly legal:

→ 1.	Fx		
2.	(∃x)Fx	1 EG	(If x has F, then something has F.)
3.	Fx→(∃x)Fx	1–2 CP	
4.	(∀x)(Fx→(∃x)Fx)	3 UG	(It is true for any x, that if x has F, then something has F.)

UG, in this case, is not used on a free variable in an assumption within the scope of that assumption. The assumption was terminated after line 2.

Restriction 4: A use of UG must quantify an entire line. You *cannot* use UG as follows:

1.	(∀x)(Ax∨Bx)		
2.	Ax∨Bx	1 UI	
3.	Ax∨(∀x)Bx	2 UG	(error)
4.	(∀x)Ax∨Bx	2 UG	(error, note the lack of parentheses)

1.	(∃y)By→Ax		
2.	(∃y)By→(∀x)Ax	1 UG	(error)
3.	(∀x)((∃y)By→Ax)	1 UG	(This is legal.)

Restriction 5: Quantify over one kind of variable at a time. Thus you cannot do the following:

1. Ax→By
2. ~AxvBy   1 Impl
3. (Ax→By)→(~AxvBy)   1–2 CP
4. (∀x)((Ax→Bx)→(~AxvBx))   3 UG   (This is an error. UG has been used on both x and y.)
5. (∀x)((Ax→By)→(~AxvBy))   3 UG   (legal)
6. (∀y)(∀x)((Ax→By→(~AxvBy)) 4 UG   (also legal)

In summary, UG is as follows:

Fx

  //(∀x)Fx   provided that UG is not

           (1) used on a singular statement, such as Fa, or
           (2) on a subscript introduced by a use of EI, or
           (3) on a variable free in an assumption, within the scope of that assumption.
           (4) A use of UG must quantify an entire line.
           (5) UG must be used on only one variable at a time.

To make sure that you understand the restrictions on these four quantifier rules, do the following set of exercises:

Exercises

(A) Find the errors in each of the following proofs.

(1) 1. (∃x)Dx
    2. Dc   1 EI

(2) 1. (∃x)Dx
    2. (∃x)Gx
    3. Dx   1 EI
    4. Gx   2 EI
    5. Dx∧Gx   3,4 Conj
    6. (∃x)(Dx∧Gx) 5 EG

(3) 1. (∃x)(AxvBx)
    2. AxvBy   1 EI
    3. (∀x)(AxvBx)   2 UG

(4) 1. (∀x)Axv(∃x)(Bx∧Cx)
    2. Axv(∃x)(Bx∧Cx)   1 UI
    3. Axv(By∧Cy)   2 EI
    4. (∀y)(Axv(By∧Cy)) 3 UG
    5. (∃x)(∀y)(Axv(By∧Cy)) 4 EG

(5) 1. (∀x)(Ax∧Bx)
    2. Ac∧Bc   1 UG
    3. Ac   2 Simp
    4. (∀x)Ax   3 UG

(6) 1. (∀x)(∃y)(AxvBy)
    2. (∃y)(AxvBy)   1 UI
    3. AxvBx   2 EI
    4. (∀x)(AxvBx)   3 UG

(7) 1. (∀x)(Cx→Dx)
    2. (∃x)Cx
    3. Cx→Dx   1 UI
    4. Cx   2 EI
    5. (∃y)Cy   3 EG

(8) 1. Ca
    2. (∀x) Cx   1 UG

(9) → 1. Ax∧Bx
   2. Ax   1 Simp
   3. (∀x)Ax   2 UG
  4. (Ax∧Bx)→(∀x)Ax   1–3 CP

(10) 1. (∃x)(Ax∧Bx)
   2. Ac∧Bd   1 EI
   3. Bd   2 Simp
   4. (∃x)Bx   3 EG

Using Conditional Proof with Quantified Statements

This section introduces nothing new about conditional proof. If there is any difficulty with conditional proof, it lies with making the right assumptions. In our previous discussion about CP it was suggested that it is generally wise to assume the antecedent of a conditional conclusion, and then try to derive the consequent. This held for any conclusion that could be converted to a conditional, such as a conclusion with the form ~p∨q. Of course, one might find in the middle of a long proof that a use of conditional proof would save some steps. And if one has to prove a statement when given no premises, either CP or IP is essential.

 Now that we have introduced quantifiers, a little more advice about making assumptions for conditional proof might prove helpful. Consider the following examples:

(1) 1. (∀x)(Ax∨Bx)→Cx) //(∀x)(Ax→Cx)
   2. (Ax∨Bx)→Cx   1 UI
 → 3. Ax
   4. Ax∨Bx   3 Add
   5. Cx   2,4 MP
   6. Ax→Cx   3–5 CP
   7. (∀x)(Ax→Cx)   6 UG

Why wasn't (∀x)Ax assumed in line 3? Well, suppose we did:

 → 3.(∀x)Ax
   4. Ax   3 UI
   5. Ax∨Bx   4 Add
   6. Cx   2,5 MP
   7. (∀x)Ax→Cx   3–6 CP

We now face a problem in line 7. The scope of (∀x) does not cover the x at C. If we proceed to quantify line 7, we get, in effect,

  8. (∀)(∀x)(Ax→Cy) 7 UG

This is legal, but we were not looking for this result.

Rule of thumb: When using CP with quantified conditional conclusions, assume the antecedent of the conclusion *without the quantifier.*

Our rule of thumb does not prohibit us from assuming quantified statements for conditional proof. For example:

(2) 1. (∀x)((Ax→Bx)→Cx)   //(∀x)(Ax→Bx)→(∃x)Cx
     2. (Ax→Bx)→Cx   1 UI
     3. (∀x)(Ax→Bx)
        4. Ax→Bx   3 UI
        5. Cx   2,4 MP
        6. (∃x)Cx   5 EG
     7. (∀x)(Ax→Bx)→(∃x)Cx   2–6 CP

It would be natural at this point to comment on the use of indirect proof when working with quantifiers. Since IP will involve the negation of quantified statements, we must first attend to one more quantifier rule. Before turning to this rule, however, we'll examine a clearer formulation of mathematical induction than was given in Chapter 1.

Mathematical Induction

Mathematical induction is an important proof technique that was introduced in a folksy way when we distinguished scientific from mathematical induction in Chapter 1. Now that predicate logic has been introduced, a more careful formulation of mathematical induction is possible. Only simple induction will be treated here.

Basis: P1 [Show that the first thing in the list has the property P.]
Induction hypothesis: (∀n)(Pn→Pn+1) [Show that for any n, if n has P,
    then n+1 has P.]
Conclusion: (∀n)Pn [Every n has P.]

Suppose we wanted to prove that the sum of the first n integers is equal to n times n+1 divided by 2. Using mathematical induction, we execute the basis step by letting n=1 and discovering that 1 times 2 divided by 2 equals 1. The induction step requires a conditional proof. In this proof, we assume that what we want to prove is true for, say, the rth case. It is our task then to show that, from this assumption, what we want to prove logically follows for the r+1st case. That is, assume:

1+2+3+ . . . +r	= r(r+1)/2	By adding r+1 to both sides, we get
1+2+3+ . . . +r+(r+1)	= r(r+1)/2 + (r+1)	This leads to
	= (r(r+1)+2(r+1))/2	which leads to
	= (r+1)(r+2)/2	And this shows that our hypothesis is true for the r+1st case.

We have now shown that the basis step is true and that the induction hypothesis is true. We may conclude that it is true for every n, that the sum of the natural numbers from 1 through n is equal to n(n+1)/2.

As noted in Chapter 1, mathematical induction is a part of deductive reasoning. To see this clearly, one need only unpack the quantified statements as follows:

P1
$(\forall n)(Pn \rightarrow Pn+1) \leftrightarrow$ $((P1 \rightarrow P2) \wedge (P2 \rightarrow P3) \wedge (P3 \rightarrow P4) \wedge \ldots)$
$//(\forall n)Pn$ $\leftrightarrow$ $(P1 \wedge P2 \wedge P3 \wedge \ldots)$

P1, the basis step, provides the first term in the conclusion. P1 and the first conjunct in the induction hypothesis will provide the second term in the conclusion by modus ponens. We now have P2 to go with the second conjunct in the induction hypothesis, P2→P3. Therefore, MP yields P3. There is nothing probabilistic about this procedure. So, again, do not confuse mathematical induction with scientific induction.

Quantifier Negation (QN)

To make this rule as easy to use as possible, I'll state it in English. To change any quantified statement to a statement with the opposite quantifier you must do the following (but do it all in moving from one line to the next):

(a) Introduce a negation sign just before the quantifier.
(b) Change the quantifier to the opposite one.
(c) Introduce a negation sign just after the quantifier.
(d) Drop any double negations resulting from (a) or (c).

Examples follow:

1.	$(\exists x)\sim Ax$	1.	$(\forall x)Ax$	1.	$\sim(\exists x)Ax$
2.	$\sim(\forall x)Ax$ 1 QN	2.	$\sim(\exists x)\sim Ax$ 1 QN	2.	$(\forall x)\sim Ax$ 1 QN

QN is an equivalence rule. It may be used on a part of a line:

1. $(\forall x)\sim Ax \rightarrow (\exists y)(Cy \wedge Dy)$
2. $\sim(\exists x)Ax$ $//(\exists y)Cy$
3. $\sim(\exists x)Ax \rightarrow (\exists y)(Cy \wedge Dy)$ 1 QN   (on the antecedent of line 1)
4. $(\exists y)(Cy \wedge Dy)$ 3,2 MP
5. $Cy \wedge Dy$ 4 EI
6. Cy 5 Simp
7. $(\exists y)Cy$ 6 EG

Don't be disturbed by the use of MP on lines 3 and 2. I realize that one must strip away quantifiers before using propositional rules, such as MP, on the internal parts of quantified statements. In this case, MP was not used on the internal parts of quantified statements. It was used on the quantified statements themselves. That is, line 3 was treated as p→q, with ~(∃x)Ax falling into the p slot, and (Ey)(Cy∧Dy) falling into the q slot. Obviously line 2 fit p. QN is also useful when using indirect proof on quantified statements.

Using Indirect Proof with Quantified Statements

A typical use of IP involves assuming the negation of the conclusion, finding a contradiction, and inferring that the conclusion is true. If the conclusion is quantified, then one often finds the assumption for IP to be the negation of a quantified statement. Examples follow:

(1) 1. (∀x)(Ax→Bx)
  2. (∀x)(Bx→Cx) //(∀x)(Ax→Cx)
  3. ~(∀x)(Ax→Cx)
  4. (∃x)~(Ax→Cx)   3 QN
  5. ~(Ax→Cx)   4 EI   (remember, EI first)
  6. Ax→Bx   1 UI
  7. Bx→Cx   2 UI
  8. Ax→Cx   6,7 HS
  9. (Ax→Cx)∧~(Ax→Cx)   8,5 Conj
  10. (∀x)(Ax→Cx)   3–9 IP

(2) 1. (∃x)(Ax∨Bx)
  2. (∀x)(Bx→Ax) //(∃x)Ax
  3. ~(∃x)Ax
  4. (∀x)~Ax   3 QN
  5. Ax∨Bx   1 EI   (EI first)
  6. Bx→Ax   2 UI
  7. ~Ax   4 UI
  8. Bx   5,7 DS
  9. Ax   6,8 MP
  10. Ax∧~Ax   9,7 Conj
  11. (∃x)Ax   3–10 IP

Proofs are getting longer than they generally were in propositional logic, but this is mainly due to quantifier manipulations.

Exercises

(B) Prove the following arguments to be valid:

(1) 1. (∀x)Ax //(∃x)Ax

(2) 1. (∃x)(Ax∧Bx) //(∃x)Ax

(3) 1. (∀x)(Ax∧Bx) //(∀x)Ax

(4) 1. (∃x)(Ax∧Bx)
   //(∃x)Ax∧(∃x)Bx

(5) 1. (∃x)Ax
   2. (∀x)(Ax→Bx) //(∃x)Bx

(6) 1. (∀x)(~Ax∨Bx)
   2. (∀x)(Bx→Cx)
   //(∀x)(Ax→Cx)

(7) 1. (∀x)~(Ax∨Bx)
   2. (∃x)~Ax //~Ac

(8) 1. (∃x)(Ax∧Bx)
   2. (∀x)(Ax→Cx)
   3. (∃x)(Ax∧Dx)
   //(∃x)(Cx∧Dx)

(9) 1. (∃x)Ax
   2. (∀x)(Ax→Bx)
   3. (∃x)~Bx
   //(∃x)~Ax∧(∃x)Bx

(10) 1. (∀x)(Ax→Bx)
   2. (∃x)(Ax∧Cx)
   3. (∀x)(Bx→Dx)
   4. (∃x)(Ax∧Ex)

(5) (∀x)(Dx→Fx)
   //(∃x)(Cx∧Fx)

(11) 1.(∀x)(Ax↔~Ax) //(∀x)(Ax∧~Ax)

(12) 1. (∀x)Ax //Ac∧Ad

(13) 1. (∀x)Ax //Ab∧(∃x)Ax

(14) 1. (∀x)Ax
   //(∃x)Ax∧(∃y)Ay

(15) 1. Aa
   2. Ab //Aa∨Ab

(16) 1. ~Ac
   2. (∀x)(Bx∨Ax) //Bc

(17) 1. (∀x)(Ax→Bx)
   2. Ad //(∃x)Bx

(18) 1. (∀x)(Ax→Bx)
   2. (∀x)(Cx→~Bx)
   3. (∃x)(Ax∧Cx) //(∃x)Zx

(19) 1. (∀x)(Ax→Bx)
   2. (∃x)(Bx→Cx)
   3. (∃x)(Ax∧Bx) //(∃x)(Ax→Cx)

(20) 1. (∀x)(Ax→Bx)
   2. (∃x)(Ax→Cx)
   3. (∀x)(Bx→Cx)
   4. ((∃x)(Cx→Dx)
   5. (∀x)(Cx→Dx) //Aa→Da

(C) Use CP in each of the following exercises:

(1) 1. (∀x)(Lx→Nx)
   //(∀x)(Lx→(Mx→Nx))

(2) No premises //(∀x)(Lx→Lx)

(3) 1. (∀x)((Lx∨Mx)→Nx)
   //(∀x)(Lx→Nx)

(4) 1. (∀x)((Lx→Nx)∧(Mx→Ox))
   //(∀x)((Lx∧Mx)→(Nx∧Ox))

(5) 1. (∀x)(Ax∧Bx)
   //(∀x)(Ax↔Bx)

(6) No premises
   //(∀x)(Bx→(∃x)Bx)

(7) No premises
   //(∀x)((Cx∧~Cx)→Q)

(8) 1. (∀x)((Ax→Bx)∧(Cx→Dx))
   //(∀x)((Ax∨Cx)→(Bx∨Dx))

(9) 1. (∀x)((Ax∨Bx)→Cx)
   2. (∀x)((Dx∨Ex)→Fx)
   3. (∀x)((Cx∧Fx)→Gx)
   //(∀x)((Ax∧Dx)→Gx)

(10) 1. (∀x)(Ax→Ex)
   2. (∀x)((Bx∧Ex)→Fx)
   3. (∀x)((Cx∧Fx)→Dx)
   //(∀x)(Ax→(Bx→(Cx→Dx)))

(D) Use IP in each of the following proofs:

(1) 1. $(\forall x)(Ax{\to}Bx)$
    2. $(\exists x)Ax$ $//(\exists x)Bx$

(2) 1. $(\forall x)(Ax{\vee}Bx)$
    2. $(\forall x)(Bx{\to}Ax)$ $//(\forall x)Ax$

(3) 1. $(\forall x)(Ax{\wedge}Bx)$ $//(\forall x)(Ax{\vee}Bx)$

(4) 1. $(\forall x)(Ax{\vee}Bx){\vee}(\forall x)Ax$
    $//(\forall x)(Ax{\vee}Bx)$

(5) 1. $(\forall x)(Ax{\to}Bx)$
    2. $(\exists x)(Ax{\wedge}Cx)$
    3. $(\forall x)({\sim}Bx{\vee}Fx)$ $//(\forall x)(Fx{\vee}{\sim}Ax)$

(6) 1. $(\forall x)(Ax{\to}Bx)$
    2. $(\forall x)(Bx{\vee}Ax)$ $//Bc$

(7) 1. $(\forall x)(Ax{\to}Dx)$
    2. $(\forall x)Ax$ $//(\forall x)Dx$

(8) 1. $(\exists x)Ax{\vee}(\forall x)Ax$ $//(\exists x)Ax$

(9) No premises
    $//(\forall x)({\sim}Ax{\vee}(Ax{\vee}Bx))$

(10) 1. $(\forall x)(Ax{\to}Bx)$
    2. $(\forall x)(Cx{\to}{\sim}Bx)$
    3. $(\exists x)(Ax{\wedge}Cx)$ $//(\forall x)(Ax{\wedge}Cx)$

(E) Use any rules introduced thus far to prove the following:

(1) 1. $(\forall x)(Lx{\vee}Lx)$ $//Lc$

(2) 1. $(\forall x)((Bx{\vee}Wx){\to}((Ax{\vee}Fx){\to}Sx))$
    $//(\forall x)(Bx{\to}(Ax{\to}Sx))$

(3) 1. $(\exists x){\sim}Ax$
    2. $(\forall x)({\sim}Cx{\wedge}Bx)$
    $//(\forall x)(((Ax{\to}Bx){\wedge}Cx){\to}Cx)$

(4) 1. $(\forall x)(Ax{\to}Bx){\vee}(\exists x)(Bx{\wedge}Cx)$
    2. $(\exists x)(Ax{\wedge}{\sim}Bx)$ $//(\exists x)Cx$

(5) 1. $(\forall x)Ax{\vee}(\exists x)(Cx{\wedge}{\sim}Dx)$
    2. $(\exists x){\sim}Ax$
    3. $(\forall x)Fx{\to}(\forall x)(Cx{\to}Dx)$
    $//(\exists x){\sim}Fx$

(6) 1. $(\forall x)Bx$ $//Aa{\to}Ba$

(7) No premises
    $//(\forall x)Ax{\to}(\forall x)(Ax{\vee}Bx)$

(8) 1. $(\forall x)({\sim}Bx{\to}Bx)$
    2. $(\exists x)Bx$ $//(\forall x)Bx$

(9) 1. $(\forall x)(Ax{\to}Bx)$
    2. $(\forall x)(Ax{\to}(Bx{\to}Cx))$
    3. $(\forall x)(Bx{\to}(Cx{\to}Dx))$
    $//(\forall x)(Ax{\to}Dx)$

(10) 1. $(\forall x){\sim}(Px{\wedge}Qx)$
    2. $(\exists x)(Px{\wedge}Qx){\vee}(\forall x)(Rx{\to}Sx)$
    3. $(\forall x){\sim}(Sx{\wedge}{\sim}Tx)$
    $//(\forall x)({\sim}Tx{\to}{\sim}Rx)$

Section 3

Proving Arguments Valid
in General Predicate Logic

Transfinite set theory constitutes the foundation of most modern mathematics. Set theory depends on the primitive concepts of element, set, and membership. At the core of set theory one finds relations. Monadic predicate logic, the subject of the previous section of this book, does not deal with relations. General predicate logic does. Anyone with an interest in mathematics should seek an understanding of the mechanisms of proof in general predicate logic. Let us begin this search with an illustration.

Georg Cantor, the discoverer of set theory, produced an extremely important proof known as the *diagonal argument*. This proof involves an infinite list with an infinite decimal expansion on each line of the list. Many students, bewildered by these "infinites," completely lose sight of the logical structure of the proof. Their bewilderment could be removed if they became more systematic in their approach to Cantor's argument. As noted in Chapter 1, Section 1 of this book, there are three steps to evaluating an argument: determine its validity, determine the truth of its premises, and establish the intelligibility of the concepts employed in the argument. Cantor's argument is a bit like the Zeno argument. Both have conclusions that most people take to be obviously false. Zeno concluded that motion is impossible. Cantor concluded that some infinite sets are larger than others.

Checking the validity of an argument is the easiest of the three steps of evaluation. The overall structure of Cantor's diagonal argument can be represented as follows:

Let   Dx = x is a decimal between 0 and 1
      Lx = x is a list with infinitely many lines (as many lines
      as there are natural numbers)
      Oxy = x is on y
To prove: It is not the case that there exists an infinite list that contains
      every decimal between 0 and 1.

Clarification: We are to prove that no such list is possible. This conclusion amounts to the claim that the decimals between 0 and 1 are too numerous to put even on an infinite list. That is, there are more decimals between 0 and 1 than there are natural numbers. That is, the set of decimals between 0 and 1 is an infinite collection that is larger in number than the set of natural numbers. Therefore, some infinite collections are larger than others.

We must operate in general predicate logic in order to symbolize what must be proved here.

To prove: $\sim(\exists x)(Lx \wedge (\forall y)(Dy \rightarrow Oyx))$
In English: It is not the case that there exists an x, such that x is an infinite
      list and for all y, if y is a decimal between 0 and 1, then y is on x.

The relation Oyx places us in general predicate logic. Note that this relation forces us to use more than one quantifier in the formula. General predicate logic is sometimes referred to as multiply-quantified logic. Cantor's proof is an indirect proof. He assumed there is a list that can capture all of the decimals between 0 and 1.

→	1. $(\exists x)(Lx \wedge (\forall y)(Dy \rightarrow Oyx))$		
	2. $Lx \wedge (y)(Dy \rightarrow Oyx)$	1 EI	
	3. $Dd \wedge \sim Odx$		(the result of a separate proof, which says that a decimal named d is not on the list)
	4. $(\forall y)(Dy \rightarrow Oyx)$	2 Simp	
	5. $Dd \rightarrow Odx$	4 UI	(substituting d for y)
	6. Dd	3 Simp	

7. Odx		5,6 MP
8. ~Odx		3,6 MP
9. Odx∧~Odx		7,8 Conj
10. ~(∃x)(Lx∧(∀y)(Dy→Oyx))		1–9 IP

The argument is valid and our purpose here is served, but I suspect you would be irritated if I left line 3 unexplained. You may skip the following if you wish and move on to the subsection on quantifier rules for general predicate logic.

Only lines 1 and 3 are not derived. Our indirect proof showed that line 1 is false. Thus, only the truth of line 3 is in question. The proof of line 3 depends on a representation of an infinite list with an infinite decimal expansion on each line of the list. This is much easier to represent graphically than it is in words. The particular decimals chosen below are like a random selection when using UI; it does not matter what they are. Any other decimals would do the job. The proof is unaffected by such choices.

Line 1	.56235471	...	Each decimal is understood to have
Line 2	.33333333	...	an infinite expansion. The decimal
Line 3	.95553401	...	exists in its entirety, despite the
Line 4	.84848484	...	fact that we cannot see it.
Line 5	.99999454	...	
Line 6	.00000000	...	The list is infinitely long. The
Line 7	.51157832	...	beginning of the first eight
Line 8	.14145918	...	lines are presented to aid you in
			following the argument.

This infinite array has a diagonal: the sequence of digits beginning with the 5 in the upper left hand corner, continuing with the 3 in the second position on line 2, the 5 in the third position on line 3, the 4 in the fourth position on line 4, and so on. The diagonal is an infinite sequence of digits. The entire diagonal exists if the list exists. The diagonal is

(G) 53549038 ...

Now consider (C), a sequence where each digit in (G) is advanced to the next higher digit:

(C) 64650149 ...

Now consider the decimal between 0 and 1, call it Dd, which results from putting a decimal point in front of (C). Dd cannot be on the list of decimals. Why not?

Each decimal in the list has a diagonal digit. If the decimal is on line n, its diagonal digit is the nth digit in the expansion. For Dd to be on the list it must possess the diagonal digit of some decimal on the list. (G) is the sequence of diagonal digits and the digits in (C) differ from every one of these. By definition, each digit in (C) is one more than the corresponding digit in (G). Thus (C) cannot have the diagonal digit of any line on the list. There exists a decimal that we have named Dd (which is C with a decimal point), that cannot be on the list. This is precisely what premise 3 of the argument asserts (i.e., Dd∧~Ody).

If you can make sense of infinite sequences and if you accept indirect proof, Cantor has got you. Some infinite collections are larger than others.

Quantifier Rules in General Predicate Logic

This subsection recapitulates the quantifier rules and adds any conditions necessary for their use in general predicate logic. Let Fxy stand for any expression containing variables x and y:

EI: $(\exists x)(\exists y)$Fxy   or $(\exists x)(\forall y)$Fxy
    $//(\exists y)$Fxy $//(\forall y)$Fxy

or any subscript other than x you wish provided that

(a) the subscript is not a proper name;
(b) the subscript is not free earlier in the proof, in which case you must choose a different one;
(c) $(\exists x)$ covers the entire line;
(d) all occurrences of x are treated in the same way;
(e) the variable x is freed by the use of EI; and
(f) only one variable is affected by the use of EI.

Illustrations of violations of these restrictions follow:

(1)   1. $(\exists x)(\exists y)$Fxy
      2. $(\exists y)$Fay   1 EI   [Violates (a), since a is a proper name. Suppose a = Alice and Fxy = x is the father of y. You'd be going from "Someone is someone's father" to "Alice is someone's father."]

      3. $(\exists y)$Fxy   1 EI
      4. Fxx   3 EI   [Violates (b), since x is free in line 3. Line 4 reads "x is the father of x."]

(2)   1. $(\exists x)(\exists y)$Fxy
      2. $(\exists x)$xy   1 EI   [Violates (c), since $(\exists y)$ is not the lead quantifier.]

(3)   1. $(\exists x)$Fxx
      2. Fxy   1 EI   [Violates (d), since the occurrences of x in line 1 were not treated alike. Suppose Fxx = x feeds x. It doesn't follow that x feeds y.]

(4) 1. (∃x)(∃y)Fxy
    2. (∃y)Fyy   1 EI   [Violates (e), since x was not freed by the use of EI. From "Someone is someone's father" it doesn't follow that "Someone is his own father."]

(5) 1. (∃y)Fxy
    2. Fzz   1 EI   [Violates (f), since both x and y were affected by one use of EI. "z is the father of z" doesn't follow from "X is the father of someone."]

UI: (∀x)(∃y)Fxy or (∀x)(∀y)Fx
     //(∃y)Fxy   //(∀y)Fxy

or any subscript you wish provided that

(a) (∀x) covers the entire line;
(b) all occurrences of x are treated alike;
(c) the occurrences of x are freed by the use of UI; and
(d) UI works on only one variable at a time.

Illustrations of violations of these restrictions follow:

(1) 1. (∃x)(∀y)Fxy
    2. (∃x)Fxy   1 IU   [Violates (a), since (∀y) doesn't cover the entire line.]

(2) 1. (∀x)Fxx
    2. Fxy   1 UI   [Violates (b), since all occurrences of x in line 1 were not treated alike. "X feeds y" doesn't follow from "Everyone feeds herself (or himself)."]

(3) 1. (∀x)(∃y)Fxy
    2. (∃y)yy   1 UI   [Violates (c), you intended to free x but bound it with (∃y). You went from "Everyone feeds someone" to "Someone feeds herself."]

(4) 1. (∀x)(∃y)Fxy
    2. (∃y)Fzz   1 UI   [Violates (d), UI was used on both x and y. You end up with a bad move which is similar to (3) above.]

EG: Fxy   or Fay   or Fxx
     //(∃x)Fxy   //(∃x)Fxy   //(∃y)Fxy

You may choose any subscript you wish for the quantifer provided

(a) you bind only one variable with one use of EG, and
(b) you do not cause a variable to be bound by a different quantifier from the one you are introducing with EG.
(c) The scope of EG must cover the entire line.

Illustrations of violations follow:

(1) 1. Fxy
    2. $(\exists x)$Fxx   1 EG   [Violates (a)."Something is fatter than itself" does not follow from "X is fatter than y."]

(2) 1. $(\forall y)$Fxy
    2. $(\exists y)(\forall y)$Fyy   1 EG   [Violates (b), the quantifier nearest the expression always takes precedence. Don't go from "X is fatter than everything" to "Everything is fatter than itself."]

(3) 1. Fx→Gy
    2. Fx→$(\exists y)$Gy   1 EG   [Violates (c), but one could make things right by replacing line 2 with $(\exists y)$(Fx→Gy).]

UG: Fxy   or   Fxy
    //$(\forall y)$Fxy   //$(\forall x)$Fxy

You may choose any subscript you wish provided

(a) you are not generalizing on a proper name;
(b) you are not generalizing on a variable which was introduced by a use of EI, or on a variable free in a line obtained by EI;
(c) you are not generalizing on a variable free in an assumption within the scope of that assumption;
(d) you bind only one variable at a time;
(e) your use of UG doesn't cause a variable to be bound by another quantifier; and
(f) all occurrences of the variable being bound are treated alike.
(g) The scope of UG must cover the entire line.

Violations follow:

(1) 1. Fay
    2. $(\forall x)$Fxy   1 UG   [Violates (a), can't generalize on one case, as in "Alice feeds y," therefore "Everyone feeds y."]

(2) 1. $(\exists x)(\forall y)$Fxy
    2. $(\forall y)$Fxy   1 EI
    3. $(\forall x)(\forall y)$Fxy   2 UG   [Violates (b), can't generalize on a variable introduced by EI, as in "Someone feeds everyone," therefore "Everyone feeds everyone."]

(3) 1. $(\forall x)(\exists y)$Fyx
    2. $(\exists y)$Fyx   1 UI
    3. Fyx   2 EI
    4.$(\forall x)$Fyx   3 UG   [Violates (b), x is free in line 3.]

5. (∃y)(∀x)Fyx   4 EG   [Obtained by a use of EI. Don't go from "Everyone has a father" (line 1) to "Someone is everyone's father." (line 5)]

(4) 1. Fxy
   2. (∀x)Fxy   1 UG   [Violates (c).]

(5) 1. Fxy
   2. (∀y)Fyy   1 UG   [Violates (d), one variable at a time. "X is the father of y" doesn't entail x is his own father.]

(6) 1. (∃x)Fxy
   2. (∀x)(∃x)Fxx   1 UG   [Violates (e), don't cause the variable you intend to bind to be bound by another variable. Something fathered y, therefore, something fathered itself?]

(7) 1. Fxx
   2. (∀y)Fxy   1 UG   [Violates (f). "Something feeds itself" does not entail that "X feeds everything."]

(8) 1. Fx→Gy
   2. Fx→(∀y)Gy   1 UG   [Violates (g), can't quantify a piece of a line.]

These seemingly nit-picking restrictions are so numerous that some people, when first introduced to general predicate logic, don't want to play anymore. But if they ignore these restrictions, they can generate invalid arguments.

The next two subsections introduce some basic logical concepts that were not available until general predicate logic and also provide additional illustrations of proofs.

At Least, At Most, and Exactly

In Section 5 of Chapter 1 The Principle of Identity was introduced—namely, $(\forall x)(\forall y)((x=y)\leftrightarrow(\forall P)(Px\leftrightarrow Py))$. Having defined identity, we can use it to sort out a few more basic logical distinctions. Suppose we wanted to translate "There is at least one cat." This is easily rendered as $(\exists x)Cx$. We now try "There are at least two cats." Will $(\exists x)(\exists y)(Cx\land Cy)$ take care of this? It will not, because it is possible that x and y are the same cat. If there are at least two cats, x and y, we must deny that x and y name the same cat.

$(\exists x)(\exists y)((Cx\land Cy)\land\sim(x=y))$

Now let us try "There is at most one cat." We cannot use $(\exists x)Cx$ because "at least one" permits the possibility of five thousand cats. We might try

(∃x)(Cx∧(∀y)(Cy→(x=y)), which tells us that there is at least one cat and that if anything else is cat it is equal to this cat. But "at most one" allows the possibility of no cats. In translating "at most one," we cannot make any existential claims. Here is a better effort:

(∀x)(Cx→(∀y)(Cy→(x=y)))

That is, if anything turns out to be a cat, then anything else that is a cat will be equal to this thing. There won't be more than one cat and there might be none.

"There is exactly one" is a combination of "at least one" and "at most one." It was given above, but we'll repeat it:

(∃x)(Cx∧(∀y)Cy→(x=y))

Given these suggestions, you might try to formulate "There are exactly two cats," "There are at most two cats," "There are exactly three cats," and so on. Each time you do a translation, retranslate it back into English, as literally as you can. You may find interesting differences between your effort and the original English. Keep tinkering with the translation until there is a match.

If there are at least two cats, is it provable that there is at least one cat? Of course it is, but could you do the proof?

1.	(∃x)(∃y)((Cx∧Cy)∧~(x=y))	//(∃x)Cx
2.	(Ey)((Cx∧Cy)∧~(x=y))	1 EI
3.	(Cx∧Cy)∧~(x=y)	2 EI
4.	Cx∧(Cy∧~(x=y))	3 Assoc
5.	Cx	4 Simp
6.	(∃x)Cx	5 EG

Some Common Properties of Relations

Three fundamental properties of relations are those of transitivity, symmetry, and reflexivity. Now that we are in general predicate logic we can capture these characteristics.

Transitive relation: (∀x)(∀y)(∀z)((Rxy∧Ryz)→Rxz)

For example, if x and y range over natural numbers, and if Gxy = x is greater than y, then Gxy is a transitive relation.

Symmetric relation: (∀x)(∀y)(Rxy→Ryx)

For example, if x and y are objects, and Rxy = x resembles y, then Rxy is a symmetric relation.

Reflexive relation: (∀x)Rxx

Obviously "equals" is reflexive. Everything equals itself.

Can we prove that intransitive relations (never transitive) are irreflexive (never reflexive)? Let's see:

1. $(\forall x)(\forall y)(\forall z)((Rxy \wedge Ryz) \rightarrow \sim Rxz)$ //$(\forall x)\sim Rxx$
2. $(\forall y)(\forall z)((Rxy \wedge Ryz) \rightarrow \sim Rxz)$ 1 UI
3. $(\forall z)((Rxx \wedge Rxz) \wedge \sim Rxz)$ 2 UI [Pick x when stripping $(\forall y)$.]
4. $(Rxx \wedge Rxx) \rightarrow \sim Rxx$ 3 UI [Pick x when stripping $(\forall z)$.]
5. $Rxx \rightarrow \sim Rxx$ 4 Taut
6. $\sim Rxx \vee \sim Rxx$ 5 Impl
7. $\sim Rxx$ 6 Taut
8. $(\forall x)\sim Rxx$ 7 UG

Can we prove that a reflexive relation is never asymmetric? (An asymmetric relation is never symmetric.) We can. For fun, let's use indirect proof:

1. $(\forall x)Rxx$ //$\sim(\forall x)(\forall y)(Rxy \rightarrow \sim Ryx)$
2. $(\forall x)(\forall y)(Rxy \rightarrow \sim Ryx)$
3. $(\forall y)(Rxy \rightarrow \sim Ryx)$ 2 UI
4. $Rxx \rightarrow \sim Rxx$ 3UI   [any subscript when using UI]
5. $\sim Rxx \vee \sim Rxx$ 4 Impl
6. $\sim Rxx$ 5 Taut
7. Rxx 1 UI
8. $Rxx \wedge \sim Rxx$ 7,6 Conj
9. $\sim(\forall x)(\forall y)(Rxy \rightarrow \sim Ryx)$ 2–8 IP

We might conclude this introduction to properties of relations by emphasizing the difference between a relation that never holds, such as an asymmetric relation, $(\forall x)(\forall y)(Rxy \rightarrow \sim Ryx)$, and a relation that doesn't always hold, such as a nonsymmetric relation, $\sim(\forall x)(\forall y)(Rxy \rightarrow Ryx)$. Similarly, a relation being intransitive, $(\forall x)(\forall y)(\forall z)((Rxy \wedge Ryz) \rightarrow \sim Rxz)$, is not the same as a relation which is nontransitive, $\sim(\forall x)(\forall y)(\forall z)((Rxy \wedge Ryz) \rightarrow Rxz)$.

Exercises

Try the following proofs. The correct answers are in the back of the book.

(1) 1. $(\exists x)(\exists y)Gxy$ //$(\exists y)(\exists x)Gxy$

(2) 1. $(\forall x)(\forall y)Gxy$ //$(\exists z)(\exists w)Gzw$

(3) 1. $(\forall x)(Gx \wedge Hx)$//$(\forall x)Gx \wedge (\forall x)Hx$

(4) 1. $(\forall x)(Gx \wedge (\forall y)Hy)$
   //$(\forall x)(\forall y)(Gx \wedge Hy)$

(5) 1. $(\forall x)(Gx \wedge (\exists y)Hy)$
   //$(\forall x)(\exists y)(Gx \wedge Hy)$

(6) 1. $(\exists x)(\forall y)(Gx \vee Hy)$
   //$(\forall y)(\exists x)(Gx \vee Hy)$

(7) 1. $(\forall x)(\forall y)(Rxy \rightarrow \sim Ryx)$
   //$(\forall x)\sim Rxx$

(8) 1. $(\forall x)(\forall y)(\forall z)((Rxy \wedge Ryz) \rightarrow Rxz)$
   2. $(\forall x)\sim Rxx$
   //$(\forall x)(\forall y)(Rxy \rightarrow \sim Ryx)$

(9) 1. $(\exists x)(\forall y)Lxy$
   2. $(\forall x)(Lxx \rightarrow (\exists y)Gyx)$
   //$(\exists z)(\exists x)Gzx$

(10) 1. $(\exists x)(\forall y)(Mxy \leftrightarrow \sim Mxy)$

$//(\forall x)(Mxx\wedge\sim Mxx)$

(11) 1. $(\forall x)(\forall y)Gxy$ $//(\forall y)(\forall x)Gxy$

(12) 1. $(\exists x)(\forall y)Gxy$ $//(\forall y)(Ey)Gxy$

(13) 1. $(\forall x)(\forall y)Gxy$ $//(\exists z)Gzz$

(14) 1. $(\forall x)(Gx\vee(\forall y)Hy)$
$//(\forall x)(\forall y)(Gx\vee Hy)$

(15) 1. $(\forall x)(Gx\vee(\exists y)Hy)$
$//(\forall x)(\exists y)(Gx\vee Hy)$

(16) 1. $(\exists x)(\forall y)(Ryx\leftrightarrow\sim Rxx)$
$//(\exists z)Tz$

(17) 1. $(\forall x)(\forall y)(\forall z)(\forall w)(\sim Gxy\rightarrow Gzw)$
$//(\forall x)Gxx$

(18) 1. $(\exists x)(Ax\wedge(Bx\wedge Cx))$
2. $(\forall x)((Ax\leftrightarrow Cx)\rightarrow(\forall y)(Dy\vee Ey))$
$//(\exists x)(Ex\vee Dx)$

(19) 1. $(\forall x)(\forall y)(\forall z)(Dxyz\rightarrow Ec)$
2. $(\exists x)(\exists y)Dcxy$
$//Ec$

(20) No premises
$//(\exists x)(Fx\wedge Gx)\rightarrow((\exists x)Fx\wedge(\exists x)Gx)$

Section 4

A Glimpse Beyond

This brief introduction to logic is not equivalent to the first course in logic. It is with some hesitation that I end this book with a topic that is beyond the first course: the problem of decidability. The great importance of this topic has led me to put my qualms aside. My qualms stem from my fear that the following account will be too brief to mean much to a reader who is just learning about logic. But what can we lose? It may make some sense. And, even if it doesn't, the only things lost are a little space on my part and a little time on your part. Here goes.

Some years ago, a man named David Hilbert wondered if there was a way to find a general procedure for solving all problems in logic and mathematics. Had computers been available to him, he would have tried to write a sequence of programs that would have solved all problems in successively more difficult levels of logic and mathematics. Recall that the concept of effectiveness involves proofs being checkable by a machine. Hilbert's plan was to discover a way to make all proofs derivable by a machine. Had he been successful, he would have put logicians and mathematicians out of business.

Hilbert died in 1943, the year that the first electronic computer was built. He had spent a good part of his life searching for sets of instructions (and computer programs are nothing more than this) that would generate proofs for successively higher levels of logic and mathematics. He began with the lowest level of logic, propositional logic. He examined the portion of propositional logic that could lead toward mathematics—the portion that contained only tautologies. No one wants statements in mathematics that might be false or that are contradictory.

Hilbert especially wanted to avoid contradictions, since with a contradiction one can trivialize mathematics and logic by proving anything in two steps. Permit a quick review: Suppose on one line of a proof you have some statement p and on another line ~p. And now consider Goldbach's conjecture, which no one has ever been able to prove: Every even number can be represented as a sum of two odd primes. Call this conjecture G. Given the contradictory claims p and ~p, we can prove G in two steps:

p
~p
p∨G   (by the rule of Addition on p)
G   (by DS on p∨G and ~p)

There is another hypothesis in mathematics called the *continuum hypothesis* (call this C), which has been proved to be unprovable. Given the contradiction above, we can prove C with the same two steps that we proved G. Hilbert's first task was to ensure that contradictions could not possibly arise in the systems of logic he examined. He needed a proof of the *consistency* of the system. He found such a proof for propositional logic.

But just what is a logical *system*? Hilbert took care to provide a precise definition of what he called a *formal system:*

(1) Specify all of the notation that may be used in the system (i.e., provide the alphabet for the system). The alphabet for our version of propositional logic consisted of symbols for statements (like A,B,C,), symbols for logical operators (like ∨ and →), and parentheses for punctuation.
(2) Specify what counts as a well-formed formula (a wff) in the system by means of recursive definition. An example of such a definition was provided in Chapter 1, Section 4.
(3) Specify the initial wffs of the system. How do you do this? Just write them down as you might set up the pieces at the beginning of a chess game. Which wffs? Any you wish; it's your game. Of course, Hilbert knew where he was going, so he didn't pick his initial wffs arbitrarily.
(4) We've set up a game, but we could not play without rules for making moves. We need a set of rules that permit us to generate new wffs from those given and any derived from those given. The rules given in Chapter 3 (such as MP, DS, and Impl) constitute such a set.
(5) We need to specify what counts as a legal result, a theorem. All initial wffs (step 3) are legal and all wffs derived by the rules specified in step 4 are legal results.

So Hilbert very carefully defined propositional logic as a formal system. He set it up so that all his initial wffs were tautologies and he picked rules that guaranteed that only tautologies could be generated from tautologies. And that is how he proved the consistency of his version of propositional logic. If you begin with tautologies and have rules that won't generate anything else, you aren't going to generate any contradictions. A system that *cannot* have contradictions is consistent.

But consistency was not enough for Hilbert. He also wanted to prove that *any* tautology that could be a wff in the system could be derived from the initial wffs by the generative rules of the system. That is, he wanted to prove the *completeness of the system.* To put it more casually, Hilbert wanted to prove that any truth that might occur in the system was guaranteed a proof (i.e., whatever is true is provable).

Proving the completeness of a system may sound easy enough, until you realize that to have a completeness proof you must come up with a general proof procedure, a program, which will automatically grind out a proof for any truth that might ever arise as a legal formula in the system. This general proof procedure is called a *decision procedure.*

Once you have a decision procedure for a level of logic, such as propositional logic, you have eliminated the need for humans to work at theorem proving at that level. Hilbert's ambition was to find consistency and completeness proofs at the lowest level of logic, which is propositional logic, then move up to monadic predicate logic and do the same, and then move on to general predicate logic. If all of mathematics can be captured in general predicate logic, and if Hilbert had found consistency and completeness proofs for unrestricted general predicate logic, he would have eliminated the need for mathematicians. Any true conjecture would have an automatic proof.

Although details of consistency and completeness proofs are well beyond this book, it would be cruel to conceal the fate of Hilbert's program from you. His program succeeded until he hit first-order general predicate logic with identity. At that level, one can express arithmetic, and at that level it becomes impossible to prove both consistency and completeness. The man who derailed Hilbert's program was Kurt Gödel, who in 1931 proved that once you had a system that could capture arithmetic you couldn't get both consistency and completeness. Some people hailed Gödel's proof as the proof that there would always be a mathematician. Whether that mathematician will be a human or a computer is a subject for another book.

Answers to Exercises

CHAPTER 1, Section 3

1. M→K
2. M→(J→K)
3. (M→J)→K
4. M↔K
5. M→K
6. K→M
7. M∨K
8. M∧K
9. ~M∧K
10. ~(M∧K) or ~M∨~K

11. ~M∨K
12. ~M∧~K or ~(M∨K)
13. ~M∨~K or ~(M∧K)
14. ~M∧~K or ~(M∨K)
15. (M∧E)→K
16. ~K→~M
17. (M→E)∧(E→M)
18. (M∧E)∨(~M∧~E)
19. ~(M→E)
20. (C∨M)∧~(C∧M)

CHAPTER 1, Section 4

1. a,e,o,p
2. a,e,o
3. a,c
4. a,d
5. a,b,h
6. a,d,g
7. a,c
8. a
9. a,b,q
10. a,b,j,t

11. a,b,j
12. a,b,j
13. a,b,h
14. a,e
15. a,b,q
16. a,b,m
17. a,d
18. a,b,j
19. a,b,q
20. a,b,h,s

CHAPTER 1, Section 5

1. (∃x)(Cx∧Bx)
2. (∃x)(Cx∧~Bx)
3. (∀x)(Cx→~Bx)
4. ~(∀x)(Cx→Bx) or 2.
5. (∀x)(Cx→Bx)
6. ~(∃x)(Cx∧Bx) or 3.
7. (∃x)(Fx∧Cx)
8. Ba
9. (∀x)(Ax→~Dx)
10. (∃x)(Sx∧~Px)

11. Or→(∃x)(Nx∧Ox)
12. (∀x)(Ix→Mx)
13. (∃x)(Sx∧~Ex)
14. Wm→Le
15. Wm→(∃x)Lx
16. (∀x)(Nx→Sx)
17. ~So
18. (∀x)(Tx→Sx)
19. (∃x)(Nx∧Ix)
20. (∃x)(Sx∧Nx) or (∃x)(Sx∧~Ex)

CHAPTER 1, Section 7

1. (∀x)(Nx→~Sox)
2. ~(∃x)(∀y)((Nx∧Ny)→Gxy)
3. (∃x)(∀y)((Nx∧Ny)→Lxy)

4. (∀x)(∀y)(∃z)((Px∧Py∧Pz)→Bzxy)
5. (∀x)(∀y)((Fx∧Sy)→(Rxy↔Ryx))
6. (∀x)(Nx→~Gxx)

7. $(\forall x)(Sx \rightarrow Sax)$
8. $(\exists x)(\forall y)((Dx \wedge Dy) \rightarrow \sim Byx)$
9. $(\forall x)(Dx \rightarrow Bxx)$
10. $(\forall x)(\forall y)((Px \wedge By \wedge Bxy) \rightarrow Fx)$
11. $(\forall x)(\forall y)((Px \wedge By \wedge \sim Bxy) \rightarrow Vx)$
12. $(\forall x)(\forall y)(\forall z)((Gxy \wedge Gyz) \rightarrow Gxz)$
13. $(\forall x)(\forall y)((Cx \wedge Ey \wedge Cxy) \rightarrow Pxy)$

14. $(\forall x)(\forall y)((Sx \wedge By) \rightarrow \sim Ixy)$
15. $\sim Lkj$
16. $(\forall x)(Px \rightarrow \sim Lkx)$
17. $(\exists x)(\forall y)((Px \wedge Hy) \rightarrow \sim Cxy)$
18. $(\exists x)(\exists y)((Bx \wedge By \wedge Bxy)$
19. $(\forall x)(\forall y)(\forall z)((Exz \wedge Eyz) \rightarrow Exy)$
20. $(\exists x)(\forall y)(Mxy \leftrightarrow \sim Myy))$

CHAPTER 2, Section 3

1. contingent
2. contingent
3. tautology
4. contradiction
5. tautology
6. tautology
7. tautology
8. tautology
9. contingent
10. tautology

11. contingent
12. tautology
13. contradiction
14. contingent
15. tautology
16. contingent
17. contingent
18. contingent
19. contradiction
20. tautology

CHAPTER 2, Section 4

1. yes
2. no
3. no
4. yes
5. no

6. no
7. yes
8. yes
9. no
10. yes

11. yes
12. yes
13. yes
14. yes
15. no

16. yes
17. no
18. yes
19. yes
20. yes

CHAPTER 3, Section 2

1.
A	B
F	T

2.
A	B
F	T

3.
A	B
F	/

4.
A	B	C	D
F	T	F	/

5.
P	Q	R	S	T	U
T	F	F	F	F	F

6.
A	B	C	D	E
F	F	T	T	T

7.
M	N
F	T

8.
C	D	E	F
T	F	T	T

9.
A	B	C
F	/	F

10.
A	B	C	D	E	F
F	F	F	F	F	F

11.
A	B	Z
T/F	T/F	F

12.
A	B	C
T	T	F

13.
P	Q	R	S	T
/	T	T	T	F

14.
A	B	C
F	/	F

15.	J	K	L	M	N
	F	F	F	F	F

18.	A	B	C	D
	F	/	F	/

16.	P	Q	R	S	T
	T	/	T	T	T

19.	A	B	C	D	E	F	G
	T	F	F	F	F	F	F

17.	A	B	C	D	E
	F	F	/	F	F

20.	A	B	C	D	E
	F	F	/	F	T

CHAPTER 3, Section 3 (A)

Each of your answers in this set should consist of a second line, 2, with the conclusion written on it (without the '//'). You should also have a justification. These are given below.

(1)	1 Impl	(11)	1 Assoc	(21)	1 Taut
(2)	1 Impl	(12)	1,2 MP	(22)	1 Simp
(3)	1 Exp	(13)	1,2 DS	(23)	1 DeM
(4)	1 Abs	(14)	1,2 HS	(24)	1 DeM
(5)	1 DN	(15)	1,2 MT	(25)	1 Trans
(6)	1 DN	(16)	1 Comm	(26)	1 Assoc
(7)	1 Taut	(17)	1 Comm	(27)	2,1 Conj
(8)	1 Taut	(18)	1 Add	(28)	2 Add
(9)	1 Dist	(19)	1 Add	(29)	1,2 MT
(10)	1 Dist	(20)	1 Add	(30)	1,2 MP

CHAPTER 3, Section 3 (B)

(1)	2. ~A∨(B→C)	1 Impl	
	3. ~A∨(~B∨C)	2 Impl	
(2)	2. ~B∨~~C	1 DN	
	3. ~(B∧~C)	2 DeM	
(3)	2. B→C	1 Impl	
	3. (B→C)∨D	2 Add	
(4)	2. (~A∨B)~(~A∨C)	1 Dist	
	3. ~A∨C	2 Simp	
(5)	2. ~A∨~A	1 Impl	
	3. ~A	2 Taut	
(6)	2. (A∨B)∨C	1 Assoc	
	3. C∨(A∨B)	2 Comm	
(7)	2. ~~(A∨B)	1 DN	
	3. ~(~A∧~B)	2 DeM	
(8)	2. A∧(B∨C)	1 Dist	
	3. A	2 Simp	
(9)	2. A→(A∧B)	1 Abs	
	3. ~A∨(A∧B)	2 Impl	
(10)	2. (A→B)∧(B→A)	1 Equiv	
	3. B→A	2 Simp	
(11)	2. (A∧B)→C	1 Exp	
	3. (B∧A)→C	2 Comm	

(12)	2. ~A∨~B	1 DeM	
	3. A→~B	2 Impl	
(13)	2. ~A∨B	1 Impl	
	3. B∨~A	2 Comm	
(14)	2. ~~A∨B	1 DN	
	3. ~A→B	2 Impl	
(15)	2. A∧A	1 Taut	
	3. (A∧A)∨(A∧A)	2 Taut	
(16)	2. (A∧B)(~A∧~B)	1 Equiv	
	3. (A∧B)∧~(A∨B)	2 DeM	
(17)	2. A→B	1 Impl	
	3. ~B→~A	2 Trans	
(18)	2. A∧A	1 Taut	
	3. (A∧A)∨B	2 Add	
(19)	2. (A∨A)∧(A∨B)	1 Dist	
	3. A∨A	2 Simp	
(20)	2. ~(A→B)∧~C	1 DeM	
	3. ~(A→B)	2 Simp	
(21)	2. ~~A∨B	1 DN	
	3. ~~A∨~~B	2 DN	
(22)	2. ~A∨(B∧C)	1 Dist	
	3. A→(B∧C)	2 Impl	

(23)	2.	~A∨B	1 Impl	(34)	3.	(A∧B)∨(~A∧~B)	1 Equiv
	3.	~A∨~~B	2 DN		4.	~A∧~B	3,2 DS
(24)	2.	~A∨(A∧B)	1 Impl	(35)	3.	~(B∧C)→D	2 DeM
	3.	(~A∨A)∧(~A∨B)	2 Dist		4.	A→D	1,3 HS
(25)	2.	(C∧B)∧A	1 Comm	(36)	3.	B→C	2 Trans
	3.	C∧(B∧A)	2 Assoc		4.	A→C	1,3 HS
(26)	2.	~~((A∧B)∧C)	1 DN	(37)	4.	B→C	1,2 DS
	3.	~(~(A∧B)∨~C)	2 DeM		5.	~B	3,4 MT
(27)	2.	~A∨B	1 Add	(38)	3.	C∨B	1 Comm
	3.	A→B	2 Impl		4.	B	3,2 DS
(28)	2.	~A∧~B	1 DeM	(39)	3.	(A∧B)∧C	2 Assoc
	3.	(~A∧~B)∨(A∧B)	2 Add		4.	D	1,3 MP
(29)	4.	A→C	3,2 HS	(40)	3.	A→~A	1,2 HS
	5.	A→D	4,1 HS		4.	~A∨~A	3 Impl
(30)	3.	A∨(B∧C)	1 Dist	(41)	3.	A→(A∧B)	1 Abs
	4.	B∧C	3,2 DS		4.	A→C	3,2 HS
(31)	3.	A→B	2,1 Impl	(42)	3.	B→(A→C)	2 Exp
	4.	A→C	3,1 HS		4.	A→(A→C)	1,3 HS
(32)	3.	B	1 Simp	(43)	3.	A∨(B∧C)	2 Add
	4.	C	2,3 MP		4.	D	1,3 MP
(33)	3.	(A∨B)∧(A∨C)	1 Conj	(44)	3.	(A∨Z)∨B	1 Add
	4.	A∨ (B∧C)	3 Dist		4.	B	3,2 DS

CHAPTER 3, Section 3 (C). Left proof: CP. Right proof: IP

(1)	2.	B		(1)	2.	~(B→D)	
	3.	B∨A	2 Add		3.	~(~B∨D)	2 Impl
	4.	A∨B	3 Comm		4.	~~B∧~D	3 DeM
	5.	C∧D	1,4 HS		5.	~~B	4 Simp
	6.	D	5 Simp		6.	~D	4 Simp
	7.	B→D	2–6 CP		7.	B	5 DN
					8.	B∨A	7 Add
					9.	A∨B	8 Comm
					10.	C∧D	1,9 MP
					11.	D	10 Simp
					12.	D∧~D	11,6 Conj
					13.	B→D	2–12 IP
(2)	2.	A∨B		(2)	2.	~((A∨B)→D)	
	3.	C∧D	1,2 MP		3.	~(~(A∨B)∨D)	2 Impl
	4.	D	3 Simp		4.	~~(A∨B)∧~D	3 DeM
	5.	(A∨B)→D	2–4 CP		5.	(A∨B)∧~D	4 DN
					6.	A∨B	5 Simp
					7.	~D	5 Simp
					8.	C∧D	1,6 MP
					9.	D	8 Simp
					10.	D∧~D	9,7 Conj
					11.	(A∨B)→D	2–10 IP

(3) ┌→ 2. A
    │ 3. A∨B   2 Add
    │ 4. C∧D   1,3 HS
    └ 5. A→(C∧D)   2–4 CP

(3) ┌→ 2. ~(A→(C∧D))
    │ 3. ~(~A∨(C∧D))   2 Impl
    │ 4. ~~A∧~(C∧D)   3 DeM
    │ 5. ~~A   4 Simp
    │ 6. A   5 DN
    │ 7. A∨B   6 Add
    │ 8. C∧D   1,7 MP
    │ 9. ~(C∧D)   4 Simp
    │ 10. (C∧D)∧~(C∧D)   8,9 Simp
    └ 11. A→(C∧D)   2–10 IP

(4) ┌→ 3. A
    │ 4. A∨B   3 Add
    │ 5. (A∨B)→(D∧E)   1,2 HS
    │ 6. D∧E   5,4 MP
    │ 7. D   6 Simp
    └ 8. A→D   3–7 CP

(4) ┌→ 3. ~(A→D)
    │ 4. (A∨B)→(D∧E)   1,2 HS
    │ ┌→5. A
    │ │ 6. A∨B   5 Add
    │ │ 7. D∧E   4,6 MP
    │ └ 8. D   7 Simp
    │ 9. A→D   5–8 CP
    │ 10. (A→D)∧~(A→D)   9,3 Conj
    └ 11. A→D   3–10 IP

(5) ┌→ 3. A
    │ 4. A→B   1 Simp
    │ 5. C→D   1 Simp
    │ 6. B   4,3 MP
    │ 7. ~D   2,6 MP
    └ 8. ~C   5,7 MT
       9. A→~C   3–8 CP
      10. ~A∨~C   9 Impl

(5) ┌→ 3. ~(~A∨~C)
    │ 4. ~~(A∧C)   3 DeM
    │ 5. A∧C   4 DN
    │ 6. A   5 Simp
    │ 7. C   5 Simp
    │ 8. A→B   1 Simp
    │ 9. C→D   1 Simp
    │ 10. B   8,6 MP
    │ 11. D   9,7 MP
    │ 12. ~D   2,10 MP
    │ 13. D∧~D   11,12 Conj
    └ 14. ~A∨~C   3–13 IP

(6) ┌→ 3. A
    │ 4. (B∧C)∨D   1,3 MP
    │ 5.~~A   3 DN
    │ 6.~(B∧C)   2,5 MT
    │ 7. D   4,6 DS
    └ 8. A→D   3–7 CP

(6) ┌→ 3. ~(A→D)
    │ 4. ~(~A∨D)   3 Impl
    │ 5. ~~A∧~D   4 DeM
    │ 6. ~~A   5 Simp
    │ 7. A   6 DN
    │ 8. ~D   5 Simp
    │ 9. (B∧C)∨D   1,7 MP
    │ 10. D∨(B∧C)   9 Comm
    │ 11. B∧C   10,8 DS
    │ 12. ~A   2,11 MP
    │ 13. A∧~A   7,12 Conj
    └ 14. A→D   3–13 IP

(7) → 4. E
    5. ~B   3,4 MP
    6. B∨C   1 Simp
    7. C   6,5 DS
    8. (~C∨~E)∧(~C∨F)   2 Dist
    9. ~C∨~E   8 Simp
    10 C→~E   9 Impl
    11. ~E   7,10 MP
    12. E→~E   4–11 CP
    13. ~E∨~E   12 Impl
    14. ~E   13 Taut
    15. ~E∨R   14 Add
    16. E→R   15 Impl

(8) → 3. A
    4. B→C   1,3 MP
    5. ~B   4,2 MT
    6. A→~B   3–5 CP
    7. ~A∨~B   6 Impl

(9) → 3. A∧C
    4. A   3 Simp
    5. C   3 Simp
    6. A→B   1 Simp
    7. C→D   1 Simp
    8. B   6,4 MP
    9. D   7,5 MP
    10. B∧D   8,9 Conj
    11. (A∧C)→(B∧D)   3–10 CP

(7) → 4. ~(E→R)
    5. ~(~E∨R)   4 Impl
    6. ~~E∧~R   5 DeM
    7. ~~E   6 Simp
    8. E   7 DN
    9. ~B   3,8 MP
    10. B∨C   1 Simp
    11. C   10,9 DS
    12. (~C∨~E)∧(~C∨E)   2 Dist
    13. ~C∨~E   12 Simp
    14. ~~C   11 DN
    15. ~E   14,13 DS
    16. E∧~E   8,15 Conj
    17. E→R   4–16 IP

(8) → 3. ~(~A∨~B)
    4. ~~(A∧B)   3 DeM
    5. A∧B   4 DN
    6. A   5 Simp
    7. B→C   1,6 MP
    8. B   5 Simp
    9. ~B   7,2 MT
    10. B∧~B   8,9 Conj
    11. ~A∨~B   3–10 IP

(9) → 3. ~((A∧C)→(B∧D))
    4. ~(~(A∧C)∨(B∧D))   3 Impl
    5. ~~(A∧C)∧~(B∧D)   4 DeM
    6. ~~(A∧C)   5 Simp
    7. A∧C   6 DN
    8. A   7 Simp
    9. C   7 Simp
    10. ~(B∧D)   5 Simp
    11. A→B   1 Simp
    12. C→D   1 Simp
    13. B   11,8 MP
    14. D   12,9 MP
    15. B∧D   13,14 Conj
    16. (B∧D)∧~(B∧D)   15,10 Conj
    17. (A∧C)→(B∧D)   3–16 IP

(10)

2.	A	
3.	B	
4.	C	
5.	D	1,2 MP
6.	C→D	4–5 CP
7.	B→(C→D))	3–6 CP
8.	A→(B→(C→D))	2–7 CP

(10)

2.	~(A→(B→(C→D)))	
3.	~(~A∨(B→(C→D)))	2 Impl
4.	~~A∧~(B→(C→D))	3 DeM
5.	~(B→(C→D))	4 Simp
6.	~(~B∨(C→D)	5 Impl
7.	~~B∧~(C→D))	6 DeM
8.	~(C→D))	7 Simp
9.	~(~C∨D)	8 Impl
10.	~~C∧~D	9DeM
11.	~~A	4 Simp
12.	A	11 DN
13.	D	1,12 MP
14.	~D	10 Simp
15.	D∧~D	13,14 Conj
16.	A→(B→(C→D))	2–15 IP

(11)

2.	A	
3.	B	1 Simp
4.	A→B	1–2 CP
5.	B	
6.	A	1 Simp
7.	B→A	5–6 CP
8.	(A→B)∧(B→A)	4,7 Conj
9.	A↔B	8 Equiv

(11)

2.	~(A↔B)	
3.	~((A∧B)∨(~A∧~B))	2 Equiv
4.	~(A∧B)∧~(~A∧~B)	3 DeM
5.	~(A∧B)	4 Simp
6.	(A∧B)∧~(A∧B)	1,5 Conj
7.	A↔B	2–6 IP

(12)

3.	~A	
4.	~(D∨E)	3,2 MT
5.	~D∧~E	4 DeM
6.	~E	5 Simp
7.	~A→~E	3–6 CP
8.	~~A∨~E	7 Impl
9.	A∨~E	8 DN

(12)

3.	~(A∨~E)	
4.	~A∧~~E	3 DeM
5.	~A	4 Simp
6.	~~E	4 Simp
7.	~(D∨E)	2,5 MT
8.	~D∧~E	7 DeM
9.	~E	8 Simp
10.	~E∧~~E	9,6 Conj
11.	A∨~E	3–10 IP

(13)

3.	~B	
4.	A∧~B	2,3 Conj
5.	~~A∧~B	4 DN
6.	~(~A∨B)	5 DeM
7.	~(A→B)	6 Impl
8.	C∧D	1,7 MP
9.	C	8 Simp
10.	~B→C	3–9 CP

(13)

3.	~(~B→C)	
4.	~(~~B∨C)	3 Impl
5.	~(B∨C)	4 DN
6.	~B∧~C	5 DeM
7.	~B	6 Simp
8.	~C	6 Simp
9.	~C∨~D	8 Add
10.	~(C∧D)	9 DeM
11.	(C∧D)∨(A→B)	1 Comm
12.	A→B	11,10 DS
13.	B	12,2 MP
14.	B∧~B	13,7 Conj
15.	~B→C	3–14 IP

(14)	3. A→B	1 Simp	(14)	3. ~(A↔C)	
	4. B→A	1 Simp		4. A→B	1 Simp
	5. B→C	2 Simp		5. B→A	1 Simp
	6. C→B	2 Simp		6. B→C	2 Simp
	7. A			7. C→B	2 Simp
	8. A→C	3,5 HS		8. A→C	4,6 HS
	9. C	8,7 MP		9. C→A	7,5 HS
	10. A→C	7–9 CP		10. (A→C)∧(C→A)	8,9 Conj
	11. C			11. A↔C	10 Equiv
	12. C→A	6,4 HS		12. (A↔C)∧~(A↔C)	11,3 Conj
	13. A	12,13 MP		13. A↔C	3–12 IP
	14. C→A	11–13 CP			
	15. (A→C)∧(C→A)	10,14 Conj			
	16. A↔C	15 Equiv			

[CP added work in (14). A direct proof would have finished on line 10.]

(15)	4. ~B		(15)	4. ~(B∨D)	
	5. ~A	1,4 MT		5. ~B∧~D	4 DeM
	6. C	3,5 DS		6. ~B	5 Simp
	7. D	2,6 MP		7. ~A	1,6 MT
	8. ~B→D	4–7 CP		8. C	3,7 DS
	9. ~~B∨D	8 Impl		9. D	2,8 MP
	10. B∨D	9 DN		10. ~D	5 Simp
				11. D∧~D	9,10 Conj
				12. B∨D	4–11 IP

(16)	3. A		(16)	3. ~(A↔~A)	
	4. ~A	1,3 MP		4. ~A∨~A	1 Impl
	5. A→~A	3–4 CP		5. ~A	4 Taut
	6. ~A			6. ~~A∨A	2 Impl
	7. A	2,6 MP		7. A∨A	6 DN
	8. ~A→A	6–7 CP		8. A	7 Taut
	9. (A→~A)∧(~A→A)	5,8 Conj		9. A∧~A	8,5 Conj
	10. A↔~A	9 Equiv		10. A↔~A	3–9 IP

[Another stupid, but legal, proof. It could have ended on line 4.]

CHAPTER 3, Section 3 (D)

(1)	4. ~B	2,1 MT	(4)	4. ~A∨~B	1 DeM
	5. B∨A	3 Comm		5. A→~B	4 Impl
	6. A	5,4 DS		6. ~~B∨C	2 DN
				7. ~B→C	6 Impl
(2)	4. ~~A∨B	1 DN		8. A→C	5,7 HS
	5. ~A→B	4 Impl			
	6. ~A→C	5,2 HS			
	7. ~A→D	6,3 HS			
			(5)	4. A∨~B	3 Add
(3)	4. ~A→C	1,2 HS		5. C	1,4 MP
	5. ~A→D	4,3 HS		6. (C→D)∧(D→C)	2 Equiv
	6. ~~A∨D	5 Impl		7. C→D	6 Simp
	7. A∨D	6 DN		8. D	7,5 MP

(6) 4. C↔D   2,1 MP
     5. (C→D)∧(D→C)   4 Equiv
     6. D→C   5 Simp
     7. D   3 Simp
     8. C   6,7 MP
     9. ~C   3 Simp
     10. C∨E   8 Add
     11. E   10,9 DS

(7) 4. B
     5. (B→(C∧D))∧((C∧D)→B)
                                          2 Equiv
     6. B→(C∧D)   5 Simp
     7. C∧D   6,4 MP
     8. D   7 Simp
     9. ~(~A∨D)   3 Impl
     10. ~~A∧~D   9 Dem
     11. ~D   10 Simp
     12. D∨E   8 Add
     13. E   12,11 DS
     14. B→E   4–13 CP

(8) 4. ~A∨~B   1 DeM
     5. A→~B   4 Impl
     6. ~C∨~~B   2 DeM
     7. ~~B∨~C   6 Comm
     8. ~B→~C   7 Impl
     9. ~~C∨~A   3 DeM
     10. ~C→~A   9 Impl
     11. A→~C   5,8 HS
     12. A→~A   11,10 HS
     13. ~A∨~A   12 Impl
     14. ~A   13 Taut

(9) 4. A
     5. B   1,4 MP
     6. C→D   2,5 MP
     7. B→C   3,4 MP
     8. C   7,5 MP
     9. D   6,8 MP
     10. A→D   4–9 CP

(10) 9. ~~A   7,8 MT
     10. ~~F   6 DN
     11. ~~C   5,10 MT
     12. A   9 DN
     13. B∨~C   2,12 MP

     14. ~C∨B   13 Comm
     15. B   14,11 DS
     16. D→E   3,15 MP
     17. ~D   16,4 MT

(11) 4. A
     5. E
     6. G
     7. A∨B   4 Add
     8. C∧D   1,7 MP
     9. C   8 Simp
     10. C∧E   9,5 Conj
     11. F   2,10 MP
     12. F∧G   11,6 Conj
     13. H   3,12 MP
     14. G→H   6–13 CP
     15. E→(G→H)   5–14 CP
     16. A→(E→(G→H))   4–15 CP

(12) 4. D
     5. ~~D   4 DN
     6. ~C   2,5 MT
     7. A∨E   3 Simp
     8. E→C   3 Simp
     9. ~E   8,6 MT
     10. E∨A   7 Comm
     11. A   10,9 DS
     12. ~B   1,11 MP
     13. ~B∨~F   12 Add
     14. ~(B∧F)   13 DeM
     15. D→~(B∧F)   4–14 CP

(13) 4. A∧~E
     5. A   4 Simp
     6. ~E   4 Simp
     7. A∨~C   5 Add
     8. ~C∨A   7 Comm
     9. C→A   8 Impl
     10. A∧B   2,9 MP
     11. B   10 Simp
     12. ~E→~D   3 Simp
     13. ~D   12,6 MP
     14. B→D   3 Simp
     15. D   14,11 MP
     16. D∧~D   15,13 Conj
     17. ~(A∧~E)   4–16 IP

(14) 4. ~(~B∨A)   2 Impl
      5. ~~B∧~A   4 DeM
      6. ~~B   5 Simp
      7. ~A   5 Simp
      8. B   6 DN
      9. (B∨C)→~D   1,7 DS
     10. B∨C   8 Add
     11. ~D   9,10 MP
     12. ~D∨A   11 Add
     13. D→A   12 Impl
     14. ~E   3,13 MP

(15)→4. B
      5. ~C   2,4 MP
      6. B→C   1 Simp
      7. C   6,4 MP
      8. C∨D   7 Add
      9. D   8,5 DS
     10. B→D   4–9 CP

(16) 4. A∨(B∧C)   1 Dist
      5. (~B∨~C)∨D   2 Assoc
      6. ~~A∨(B∧C)   4 DN
      7. ~A→(B∧C)   6 Impl
      8. ~(B∧C)∨D   5 DeM
      9. (B∧C)→D   8 Impl
     10. ~A→D   7,9 HS
     11. ~D∨(E∧F)   3 Dist
     12. D→(E∧F)   11 Impl
     13. ~A→(E∧F)   10,12 HS
     14. ~(E∧F)→~~A   13 Trans
     15. ~(E∧F)→A   14 DN

(17) 4. ~A∧B   1,2 MP
      5. ~A   4 Simp
      6. ~A∨B   5 Add
      7. A→B   6 Impl
      8. D   3,7 MP

(18) 4. ~A∧~B   1 DeM
      5. ~B   4 Simp
      6. D∧E   2,5 DS
      7. D   6 Simp
      8. ~(A→C)   3,7 MP
      9. ~(~A∨C)   8 Impl
     10. ~~A∧~C   9 DeM
     11. ~~A   10 Simp
     12. A   11 DN

(19)→4. E
      5. ~~E   4 DN
      6. ~D   3,5 MT
      7. D∨~C   2 Comm
      8. ~C   7,6 DS
      9. (A∨B)∧(A∨C)   1 Dist
     10. A∨C   9 Simp
     11. C∨A   10 Comm
     12. A   11,8 DS
     13. E→A   4–12 CP

(20) 9. ~K   8 Simp
     10. J→K   6 Simp
     11. ~J   10,9 MT
     12. I→J   6 Simp
     13. ~I   12,11 MT
     14. H→I   5 Simp
     15. ~H   14,13 MT
     16. ~H∧~K   15,9 Conj
     17. L   7,16 MP
     18. L→G   8 Simp
     19. G   18,17 MP
     20. G→H   5 Simp
     21. ~G   20,15 MT
     22. G∨(F↔I)   19 Add
     23. F↔I   22,21 DS

CHAPTER 4, Section 1

(1) Aa   Ab
      T   F
(2) A   B
   a F   /
   b T   T
(3) A   B
   a T   F

(4) Aa   Ab
      F   T
(5) A   B
   a F   F
(6) A   B   C   D
   a F   F   F   /
   b T   /   T   T

(7)	A	B	C	D	
a	T	F	F	F	
(8)	A	B	C	D	E
a	F	/	T	T	T
(9)	A	B	C	D	E
a	F	F	F	F	F
(10)	A	B	C	D	
a	F	T	T	T	
b	T	F	/	/	
(11)	A	B			
a	T	F			
(12)	A	B			
a	F	/			
(13)	Aa	Ab			
	T	F			
(14)	A	B			
a	T	F			
b	F	T			

(15)	C	D			
a	T	T			
b	F	T			
(16)	A	B	C		
a	F	F	T		
b	T	T	F		
(17)	A	C	D		
a	T	T	F		
b	F	/	F		
(18)	A	B	C		
a	F	T	T		
b	T	T	T		
(19)	A	B	C	D	E
a	F	F	F	F	F
(20)	A	B	C	D	E
a	T	F	/	T	T
b	T	T	T	T	T
c	F	F	/	F	/

CHAPTER 4, Section 2 (A)

(1)   line 2: can't choose a proper name as a subscript in EI
(2)   line 4: x is free in line 3, so can't use EI with x
(3)   line 2: treat both x's in line 1 alike
        line 3: can't use UG on variable introduced by EI
        line 3: quantify only one variable at a time
(4)   line 2: can't use UI on a part of a line
        line 3: can't use EI on a part of a line
        line 4: can't use UG on a variable introduced by EI
(5)   line 4: can't use UG on a proper name
(6)   line 3: x is free in line 2, so can't use EI on x
        line 4: can't use UG on a variable introduced by EI
(7)   line 4: x is free in line 3, can't use EI on x
(8)   line 2: can't use UG on a proper name
(9)   line 3: can't use UG on variable free in assumption within the scope of that
        assumption
(10) line 2: can't choose proper name when using EI
        line 2: can't treat the x's in line 1 differently

CHAPTER 4, Section 2 (B)

(1)   2. Ax   1 UI
       3. $(\exists x)$Ax   2 EG

(2)   2. Ax∧Bx   1 EI
       3. Ax   2 Simp
       4. $(\exists x)$Bx   3 EG

(3)   2. Ax∧Bx   1 UI
       3. Ax   2 Simp
       4. $(\forall x)$Ax   3 UG

(4)   2. Ax∧Bx   1 EI
       3. Ax   2 Simp
       4. Bx   2 Simp
       5. $(\exists x)$Ax   3 EG

6. (∃x)Bx   4 EG
7. (∃x)Ax∧(∃x)Bx   5,6 Conj

(5) 3. Ax   1 EI
4. Ax→Bx   2 UI
5. Bx   4,3 MP
6. (∃x)Bx   5 EG

(6) 3. ~Ax∨Bx   1 UI
4. Bx→Cx   2 UI
5. Ax→Bx   3 Impl
6. Ax→Cx   5,4 HS
7. (∀x)(Ax→Cx)   6 UG

(7) 3. ~(Ac∨Bc)   1 UI
4. ~Ac∧~Bc   3 DeM
5. ~Ac   4 Simp

(8) 4. Ax∧Dx   3 EI
5. Ax   4 Simp
6. Dx   4 Simp
7. Ax→Cx   2 UI
8. Cx   7,5 MP
9. Cx∧Dx   8,6 Conj
10. (∃x)(Cx∧Dx)   9 EG

(9) 4. Ax   1 EI
5. Ax→Bx   2 UI
6. Bx   5,4 MP
7. (∃x)Bx   6 EG
8. ~By   3 EI
9. Ay→By   2 UI
10. ~Ay   9,8 MT
11. (∃x)~Ax   10 EG
12. (∃x)~Ax∧(∃x)Bx   11,7 Conj

(10) 6. Ax∧Cx   2 EI
7. Ax→Bx   1 UI
8. Bx→Dx   3 UI
9. Dx→Fx   5 UI
10. Ax→Dx   7,8 HS
11. Ax→Fx   10,9 HS
12. Ax   6 Simp
13. Fx   11,12 MP
14. Cx   6 Simp
15. Cx∧Fx   14,13 Conj
16. (∃x)(Cx∧Fx)   15 EG

(11) 2. Ax↔~Ax   1 UI
3. (Ax∧~Ax)∨(~Ax∧~~Ax)   2 Equiv
4. (Ax∧~Ax)∨(~Ax∧Ax)   3 DN
5. (Ax∧~Ax)∨(Ax∧~Ax)   4 Comm
6. Ax∧~Ax   5 Taut
7. (∀x)(Ax∧~Ax)   6 UG

(12) 2. Ac   1 UI
3. Ad   1 UI
4. Ac∧Ad   2,3 Conj

(13) 2. Ab   1 UI
3. (∃x)Ax   2 EG
4. Ab∧(∃x)Ax   2,3 Conj

(14) 2. Ax   1 UI
3. Ay   1 UI
4. (∃x)Ax   2 EG
5. (∃y)Ay   3 EG
6. (∃x)Ax∧(∃y)Ay   4,5 Conj

(15) 3. Aa∨Ab   1 Add

(16) 3. Bc∨Ac   2 UI
4. Ac∨Bc   3 Comm
5. Bc   1,4 DS

(17) 3. Ad→Bd   1 UI
4. Bd   3,2 MP
5. (∃x)Bx   4 EG

(18) 4. Ax∧Cx   3 EI
5. Ax   4 Simp
6. Cx   4 Simp
7. Ax→Bx   1 UI
8. Cx→~Bx   2 UI
9. Bx   7,5 MP
10. ~Bx   8,6 MP
11. Bx∨(∃x)Zx   9 Add
12. (∃x)Zx   11,10 DS

(19) 4. Bx→Cx   2 EI
5. Ax→Bx   1 UI
6. Ax→Cx   5,4 HS
7. (∃x)(Ax→Cx)   6 EG

(20) 6. Aa→Ba   1 UI
     7. Ba→Ca   3 UI
     8. Ca→Da   5 UI
     9. Aa→Ca   6,7 HS
    10. Aa→Da   9,8 HS

CHAPTER 4, Section 2 (C)

(1) 2. Lx→Nx   1 UI
    3. Lx
    4. Mx
    5. Nx   3,2 MP
    6. Mx→Nx   4–5 CP
    7. Lx→(Mx→Nx)   2–6 CP
    8. (∀x)(Lx→(Mx→Nx))
                 7 UG

(2) 1. Lx
    2. Lx∨Lx   1 Taut
    3. Lx   2 Taut
    4. Lx→Lx   1–3 CP
    5. (∀x)(Lx→Lx)   4 UG

(3) 2. (Lx∨Mx)→Nx   1 UI
    3. Lx
    4. Lx∨Mx   3 Add
    5. Nx   2,4 MP
    6. Lx→Nx   3–5 CP
    7. (∀x)(Lx→Nx)   6 UG

(4) 2. (Lx→Nx)∧(Mx→Ox)
                 1 UI
    3. Lx→Nx   2 Simp
    4. Mx→Ox   2 Simp
    5. Lx∧Mx
    6. Lx   5 Simp
    7. Mx   5 Simp
    8. Nx   3,6 MP
    9. Ox   4,7 MP
   10. Nx∧Ox   8,9 Conj
   11. (Lx∧Mx)→(Nx∧Ox)
                 5,10 CP
   12. (∀x)((Lx∧Mx)→(Nx∧Ox))
                 11 UG

(5) 2. Ax∧Bx   1 UI
    3. Ax
    4. Bx   2 Simp
    5. Ax→Bx   3–4 CP
    6. Bx
    7. Ax   2 Simp
    8. Bx→Ax   6–7 CP
    9. (Ax→Bx)∧(Bx→Ax)
                 5,8 Conj
   10. Ax↔Bx   9 Equiv
   11. (∀x)(Ax↔Bx)   10 UG

(6) 1. Bx
    2. (∃x)Bx   1 EG
    3. Bx→(∃x)Bx   1–2 CP
    4. (∀x)(Bx→(∃x)Bx)   3 UG

(7) 1. Cx∧~Cx
    2. Cx   1 Simp
    3. ~Cx   1 Simp
    4. Cx∨Q   2 Add
    5. Q   4,3 DS
    6. (Cx∧~Cx)→Q   1–5 CP
    7. (∀x)((Cx∧~Cx)→Q) 6 UG

(8) 2. (Ax→Bx)∧(Cx→Dx) 1 UI
    3. Ax∨Cx
    4. Ax→Bx   2 Simp
    5. Cx→Dx   2 Simp
    6. ~~Ax∨Cx   3 DN
    7. ~Ax→Cx   6 Impl
    8. ~Ax→Dx   7,5 HS
    9. ~Bx→~Ax   4 Trans
   10. ~Bx→Dx   9,8 HS
   11. ~~Bx∨Dx   10 Impl
   12. Bx∨Dx   11 DN
   13. (Ax∨Cx)→(Bx∨Dx)
                 3–11 CP
   14. (∀x)((Ax∨Cx)→(Bx∨Dx))
                 13 UG

(9)   4. (Ax∨Bx)→Cx   1 UI
       5. (Dx∨Ex)→Fx   2 UI
       6. (Cx∧Fx)→Gx   3 UI
→   7. Ax∧Dx
       8. Ax   7 Simp
       9. Dx   7 Simp
    10. Ax∨Bx   8 Add
    11. Cx   4,10 MP
    12. Dx∨Ex   9 Add
    13. Fx   5,12 MP
    14. Cx∧Fx   11,13 Conj
    15. Gx   6,14 MP
    16. (Ax∧Dx)→Gx   7–15 CP
    17. (∀x)((Ax∧Dx)→Gx) 16 UG

(10) 4. Ax→Ex   1 UI
       5. (Bx∧Ex)→Fx   2 UI
       6. (Cx∧Fx)→Dx   3 UI
→   7. Ax
→   8. Bx
→   9. Cx
    10. Ex   4,7 MP
    11. Bx∧Ex   8,10 Conj
    12. Fx   5,11 MP
    13. Cx∧Fx   9,12 Conj
    14. Dx   6,13 MP
    15. Cx→Dx   9–14 CP
    16. Bx→(Cx→Dx)   8–15 CP
    17. Ax→(Bx→(Cx→Dx))
                          7–16 CP
    18. (∀x)(Ax→(Bx→(Cx→Dx)))
                          17 UG

CHAPTER 4, Section 2 (D)

(1) 3. ~(∃x)Bx
     4. Ax   2 EI
     5. Ax→Bx   1 UI
     6. Bx   5,4 MP
     7. (∃x)Bx   6 EG
     8. (∃x)Bx∧~(∃x)Bx   7,3 Conj
     9. (∃x)Bx   3–8 IP

(2) 3. ~(∀x)Ax
     4. (∃x)~Ax   3 QN
     5. ~Ax   4 EI
     6. Ax∨Bx   1 UI
     7. Bx→Ax   2 UI
     8. Bx   6,5 DS
     9. Ax   7,8 MP
    10. Ax∧~Ax   9,5 Conj
    11. (∀x)Ax   3–10 IP

(3) 2. ~(∀x)(Ax∨Bx)
     3. (∃x)~(Ax∨Bx)   2 QN
     4. ~(Ax∨Bx)   3 EI
     5. ~Ax∧~Bx   4 DeM
     6. Ax∧Bx   1 UI
     7. Ax   6 Simp
     8. ~Ax   5 Simp
     9. Ax∧~Ax   7,8 Conj
    10. (∀x)(Ax∨Bx)   2–9 IP

(4) 2. ~(∀x)(Ax∨Bx)
     3. (∀x)Ax   1,2 DS
     4. Ax   3 UI
     5. Ax∨Bx   4 Add
     6. (∀x)(Ax∨Bx)   5 UG
     7. (∀x)(Ax∨Bx)∧~(∀x)(Ax∨Bx)
                          6,2 Conj
     8. (∀x)(Ax∨Bx)   2–7 IP

(5) 4. ~(∀x)(Fx∨~Ax)
     5. (∃x)~(Fx∨~Ax)   4 QN
     6. ~(Fx∨~Ax)   5 EI
     7. ~Fx∧~~Ax   6 DeM
     8. ~Fx   7 Simp
     9. ~~Ax   7 Simp
    10. Ax   9 DN
    11. Ax→Bx   1 UI
    12. Bx   11,10 MP
    13. ~Bx∨Fx   3 UI
    14. Fx∨~Bx   13 Comm
    15. ~Bx   14,8 DS
    16. Bx∧~Bx   12,15 Conj
    17. (∀x)(Fx∨~Ax)   4–16 IP

(6) ┌→ 3. ~Bc
│   4. Ac→Bc   1 UI
│   6. ~Ac   4,3 MT
│   7. BcvAc   2 UI
│   8. Ac   7,3 DS
└   9. Ac∧~Ac   8,6 Conj
    10. Bc   3–9 IP

(7) ┌→ 3. ~(∀x)Dx
│   4. Ax→Dx   1 UI
│   5. Ax   2 UI
│   6. Dx   4,5 MP
│   7. (∀x)Dx   6 UG
└   8. (∀x)Dx∧~(∀x)~Dx   7,3 Conj
     9. (∀x)Dx   3–8 IP

(8) ┌→ 2. ~(∃x)Ax
│   3. (∀x)Ax   1,2 DS
│   4. Ax   3 UI
│   5. (∃x)Ax   4 EG
└   6. (∃x)Ax∧~(∃x)Ax   5,2 Conj
     7. (∃x)Ax   2–6 IP

(9) ┌→ 1. ~(∀x)(~Axv(AxvBx))
│   2. (∃x)~(~Axv(AxvBx))
│   1 QN
│   3. ~(~Axv(AxvBx))   2 EI
│   4. ~~Ax∧~(AxvBx)   3 DeM
│   5. ~~Ax   4 Simp
│   6. ~(AxvBx)   4 Simp
│   7. ~Ax∧~Bx   6 DeM
│   8. ~Ax   7 Simp
└   9. ~Ax∧~~Ax   8,5 Conj
    10. (∀x)(~Axv(AxvBx)) 1–9 IP

(10) ┌→ 4. ~(∀x)(Ax∧Cx)
│   5. Ax∧Cx   3 EI
│   6. Ax→Bx   1 UI
│   7. Cx→~Bx   2 UI
│   8. Ax   5 Simp
│   9. Cx   5 Simp
│   10. Bx   6,8 MP
│   11. ~Bx   7,9 MP
└   12. Bx∧~Bx   10,11 Conj
    13. (∀x)(Ax∧Cx)   4–12 IP

CHAPTER 4, Section 2 (E)

(1)   2. LcvLc   1 UI
       3. Lc   2 Taut

(2)   2. (BxvWx)→((AxvFx)→Sx)
                                   1 UI
   ┌→ 3. Bx
   │┌→ 4. Ax
   ││ 5. BxvWx   3 Add
   ││ 6. (AxvFx)→Sx   5,2 MP
   ││ 7. AxvFx   4 Add
   │└ 8. Sx   6,7 MP
   └   9. Ax→Sx   4–8 CP
      10. Bx→(Ax→Sx)   3–9 CP
      11. (∀x)(Bx→(Ax→Sx)) 10 UG

(3) ┌→ 3. (Ax→Bx)∧Cx
└   4. Cx   3 Simp
      5. ((Ax→Bx)∧Cx)→Cx
                                   3–4 CP
      6. (∀x)(((Ax→Bx)∧Cx)→Cx)
                                   5 UG

(4)   3. Ax∧~Bx   2 EI
       4. ~~Ax∧~Bx   3 DN
       5. ~(~AxvBx)   4 DeM
       6. ~(Ax→Bx)   5 Impl
       7. (∃x)~(Ax→Bx)   6 EG
       8. ~(∀x)(Ax→Bx)   7 QN
       9. (∃x)(Cx∧Dx)   1,8 DS
      10. Cy∧Dy   9 EI
      11. Cy   10 Simp
      12. (∃x)Cx   11 EG

(5)   4. ~(∀x)Ax   2 QN
       5. (∃x)(Cx∧~Dx)   1,4 DS
       6. Cx∧~Dx   5 EI
       7. ~~Cx∧~Dx   6 DN
       8. ~(~CxvDx)   7 DeM
       9. ~(Cx→Dx)   8 Impl
      10. (∃x)~(Cx→Dx)   9 EG
      11. ~(∀x)(Cx→Dx)   10 QN
      12. ~(∀x)Fx   3,11 MT
      13. (∃x)~Fx   12 QN

(6)   2. Ba   1 UI
       3. Bav~Aa   2 Add

4.	~Aa∨Ba	3 Comm
5.	Aa→Ba	4 Impl

(7) ┌→ 1. (∀x)Ax
    │   2. Ax   1 UI
    │   3. Ax∨Bx   2 Add
    └── 4. (∀x)(Ax∨Bx)   3 UG
        5. (∀x)Ax→(x)(Ax∨Bx)
                             1–4 CP

(8) 3. ~Bx→Bx   1 UI
     4. ~~Bx∨Bx   3 Impl
     5. Bx∨Bx   4 DN
     6. Bx   5 Taut
     7. (∀x)Bx   6 UG

(9) 4. Ax→Bx   1 UI
     5. Ax→(Bx→Cx)   2 UI
     6. Bx→(Cx→Dx)   3 UI

7.	A→(Ax∧Bx)	4 Abs
8.	(Ax∧Bx)→Cx	5 Exp
9.	Ax→Cx	7,8 HS
10.	Ax→(Ax∧Cx)	9 Abs
11.	Ax→(Cx→Dx)	4,6 HS
12.	(Ax∧Cx)→Dx	11 Exp
13.	Ax→Dx	10,12 HS
14.	(∀x)(Ax→Dx)	13 UG

(10) 4. ~(∃x)(Px∧Qx)   1 QN
      5. (∀x)(Rx→Sx)   2,4 DS
      6. Rx→Sx   5 UG
      7. ~(Sx∧~Tx)   3 UG
      8. ~Sx∨~~Tx   7 Dem
      9. ~Sx∨Tx   8 DN
     10. Sx→Tx   9 Impl
     11. Rx→Tx   6,10 HS
     12. ~Tx→~Rx   11 Trans
     13. (∀x)(~Tx→Rx)   12 UG

CHAPTER 4, Section 3.

(1) 2. (∃y)Gxy   1 EI
     3. Gxy   2 EI
     4. (∃x)Gxy   3 EG
     5. (∃y)(∃x)Gxy   4 EG

(2) 2. (∀y)Gzy   1 UI
     3. Gzw   2 UI
     4. (∃w)Gzw   3 EG
     5. (∃z)(∃w)Gzw   4 EG

(3) 2. Gx∧Hx   1 UI
     3. Gx   2 Simp
     4. Hx   2 Simp
     5. (∀x)Gx   3 UG
     6. (∀x)Hx   4 UG
     7. (∀x)Gx∧(∀x)Hx   5,6 Conj

(4) 2. Gx∧(∀y)Hy   1 UI
     3. Gx   2 Simp
     4. (∀y)Hy   2 Simp
     5. Hy   4 UI
     6. Gx∧Hy   3,5 Conj
     7. (∀y)(Gx∧Hy)   6 UG
     8. (∀x)(∀y)(Gx∧Hy)   7 UG

(5) 2. Gx∧(∃y)Hy   1 UI
     3. Gx   2 Simp

     4. (∃y)Hy   2 Simp
     5. Hy   4 EI
     6. Gx∧Hy   3,5 Conj
     7. (∃y)(Gx∧Hy)   6 EG
     8. (∀x)(∃y)(Gx∧Hy)   7 UG

(6) 2. (∀y)(Gx∨Hy)   1 UI
     3. Gx∨Hy   2 UI
     4. (∃x)(Gx∨Hy)   3 EG
     5. (∀y)(∃x)(Gx∨Hy)   4 UG

(7) 2. (∀y)(Rxy→~Ryx)   1 UI
     3. Rxx→~Rxx   2 UI
     4. ~Rxx∨~Rxx   3 Impl
     5. ~Rxx   4 Taut
     6. (∀x)~Rxx   5 UG

(8) 3. (∀y)(∀z)((Rxy∧Ryz)→Rxz)
                            1 UI
     4. (∀z)((Rxy∧Ryz)→Rxz) 3 UI
     5. (Rxy∧Ryx)→Rxx   4 UI
     6. ~Rxx   2 UI
     7. ~(Rxy∧Ryx)   5,6 MT
     8. ~Rxy∨~Ryx   7 DeM
     9. Rxy→~Ryx   8 Impl
    10. (∀y)(Rxy→~Ryx)   9 UG
    11. (∀x)(∀y)(Rxy→~Ryx) 10 UG

(9) 3. (∀y)Lxy   1 EI
     4. Lxx   3 UI
     5. Lxx→(∃y)Gyx   2 UI
     6. (∃y)Gyx   5,4 MP
     7. Gzx   6 EI
     8. (∃x)Gzx   7 EG
     9. (∃z)(∃x)Gzx   8 EG

(10) 2. (∀y)(Mxy↔~Mxy)   1 EI
     3. Mxx↔~Mxx   2 UI
     4. (Mxx∧~Mxx)∨(~Mxx∧~~Mxx)
                           3 Equiv
     5. (Mxx∧~Mxx)∨(~Mxx∧Mxx)
                           4 DN
     6. (Mxx∧~Mxx)∨(Mxx∧~Mxx)
                           5 Comm
     7. Mxx∧~Mxx   6 Taut
     8. (∀x)(Mxx∧~Mxx)   7 UG

(11) 2. (∀y)Gxy   1 UI
     3. Gxy   2 UI
     4. (∀x)Gxy   3 UG
     5. (∀y)(∀x)Gxy   4 UG

(12) 2. (∀y)Gxy   2 EI
     3. Gxy   3 UI
     4. (∃y)Gxy   4 EG
     5. (∀y)(∃y)Gxy   5 UG
[(∀y) does nothing here, but it is legal.]

(13) 2. (∀y)Gzy   1 UI
     3. Gzz   2 UI
     4. (∃z)Gzz   3 EG

(14)┌ 2. ~(∀x)(∀y)(Gx∨Hy)
    │ 3. (∃x)~(∀y)(Gx∨Hy)   2 QN
    │ 4. (∃x)(∃y)~(Gx∨Hy)   3 QN
    │ 5. (∃y)~(Gx∨Hy)   4 EI
    │ 6. ~(Gx∨Hy)   5 EI
    │ 7. ~Gx∧~Hy   6 DeM
    │ 8. ~Gx   7 Simp
    │ 9. ~Hy   7 Simp
    │ 10. Gx∨(∀y)Hy   1 UI
    │ 11. (∀y)Hy   10,8 DS
    │ 12. Hy   11 UI
    │ 13. Hy∧~Hy   12,9 Conj
    └ 14. (∀x)(∀y)(Gx∨Hy)   2–13 IP

(15)┌ 2. ~(∀x)(∃y)(Gx∨Hy)
    │ 3. (∃x)~(∃y)(Gx∨Hy)   2 QN
    │ 4. (∃x)(∀y)~(Gx∨Hy)   3 QN
    │ 5. (∀y)~(Gx∨Hy)   4 EI
    │ 6. ~(Gx∨Hy)   5 UI
    │ 7. ~Gx∧~Hy   6 DeM
    │ 8. ~Gx   7 Simp
    │ 9. ~Hy   7 Simp
    │ 10. Gx∨(∃y)Hy   1 UI
    │ 11. (∃y)Hy   10,8 DS
    │ 12. (∀x)~Hy   9 UG
    │ 13. ~(∃y)Hy   12 QN
    │ 14. (∃y)Hy∧~(∃y)Hy   11,13 Conj
    └ 15. (∀x)(∃y)(Gx∨Hy)   3–14 IP

(16) 2. (∀y)(Ryx↔~Rxx)   1 EI
     3. Rxx↔~Rxx   2 UI
     4. (Rxx∧~Rxx)∨(~Rxx∧~~Rxx)
                           3 Equiv
     5. (Rxx∧~Rxx)∨(~Rxx∧Rxx)
                           4 DN
     6. (Rxx∧~Rxx)∨(Rxx∧~Rxx)
                           5 Comm
     7. Rxx∧~Rxx   6 Taut
     8. Rxx   7 Simp
     9. ~Rxx   7 Simp
     10. Rxx∨(∃z)Tz   9 Add
     11. (∃z)Tz   10,9 DS

(17) 2. (∀y)(∀z)(∀w)(~Gxy→Gzw)
                           1 EI
     3. (∀z)(∀w)(~Gxx→Gzw)
                           2 UI
     4. (∀w)(~Gxx→Gxw)   3 UI
     5. ~Gxx→Gxx   4 UI
     6. ~~Gxx∨Gxx   5 Impl
     7. Gxx∨Gxx   6 DN
     8. Gxx   7 Taut
     9. (∀x)Gxx   8 UG

(18) 3. Ax∧(Bx∧Cx)   1 EI
     4. (Ax↔Cx)→(∀y)(Dy∨Ey)
                           2 UI
     5. Ax   3 Simp
     6. (Ax∧Bx)∧Cx   3 Assoc
     7. Cx   4 Simp
     8. Ax∧Cx   5,7 Conj

9. $(Ax \land Cx) \lor (\sim Ax \land \sim Cx)$
        8 Add
10. $A \leftrightarrow Cx$ 9 Equiv
11. $(\forall y)(Dy \lor Ey)$ 4,10 DS
12. $Dy \lor Ey$ 11 UI
13. $Ey \lor Dy$ 12 Comm
14. $(\forall x)(Ex \lor Dx)$ 13 UG

(19) 3. $(\exists y)Dcxy$ 2 EI
   4. $Dcxy$ 3 EI
   5. $(\forall y)(\forall z)(Dcycz \to Ec)$ 1 UI
   6. $(\forall z)(Dcxz \to Ec)$ 5 UI
   7. $Dcxy \to Ec$ 6 UI
   8. Ec 7,4 MP

(20) 1. $(\exists x)(Fx \land Gx)$
   2. $Fx \land Gx$ 1 EI
   3. Fx 2 Simp
   4. Gx 2 Simp
   5. $(\exists x)Fx$ 3 EG
   6. $(\exists x)Gx$ 4 EG
   7. $(\exists x)Fx \land (\exists x)Gx$ 5,6 Conj
   8. $(\exists x)(Fx \land Gx) \to$
    $((\exists x)Fx \land (\exists x Gx)$ 1–7 CP

Glossary

absorption (Abs): A rule of inference that permits you to write an expression of the form p→(p∧q) provided you already have an expression of the form p→q.

addition (Add): A rule of inference that permits you to write p∨q if you already have p.

antecedent: The p part of p→q (i.e., the "if" part of a conditional statement).

argument: Two or more statements where one is said to follow from the other(s).

argument form: A structure where logical operators connect place holders for statements, instead of statements. p∨q and ~p, therefore q is an argument form. "Either they fought or they died" and "They did not fight," therefore "They died" is an instance of this form. See Chapter 2, Section 4.

association (Assoc): A rule that permits you to shift parentheses to regroup or-statements or and-statements. For example, one can replace p∨(q∨r) with (p∨q)∨r.

biconditional: Another name for a statement that is an equivalence (i.e., a statement with the form p↔q, or, to show the double conditional more clearly, the form (p→q)∧(q→p)).

Boolean conjunctive normal form (BCNF): See Chapter 2, Section 5.

Boolean disjunctive normal form (BDNF): See Chapter 2, Section 5.

bound variable: A variable falling within the scope of a quantifier (e.g., in (∀x)(Ax→Bx) the x subscripts at A and B are both bound by the quantifier (∀x). In Ax→Bx, neither the x at A nor the x at B is bound). See "free variable."

commutation (Comm): A rule that permits you to flip expressions about or-signs or and-signs (e.g., from p∨q to q∨p).

completeness (deductive) of a formal system: A guarantee that every truth expressible in the system can be proved in the system.

conclusion: The statement that is said to follow from the others in an argument.

conditional proof (CP): A demonstration that the rules will produce a certain result, q, from a given assumption, p (and any other lines already given). A conditional proof always yields a single line of the form p→q.

conditional statement: An implication statement (i.e., an "if, then" statement (i.e., a statement with the form p→q)).

conjunction: An and-statement, a statement with the form p∧q.

conjunction (Conj): A rule that lets you put an "∧" between two statements you already possess. If p is true and q is true, then p∧q is true.

conjunctive normal form (CNF): A standard form for all expressions in propositional logic. See Chapter 2, Section 5.

consequent: The q part of p→q (i.e., the "then" part of a conditional statement).

consistency of a formal system: A guarantee that a contradiction cannot be generated in the system.

constructive proof: A proof that generates the object that is claimed to exist; a proof that does not employ the Law of the Excluded Middle.

contingent statement: One whose truth table has at least one T and one F (i.e., it is true in at least one possible world and false in at least one other world).

contradiction: A statement with a truth table that always calculates to F (i.e., one that is false in all possible worlds).

decision procedure: A mechanical method that will determine in a finite number of steps whether any given formula is a theorem of a system.

deductive argument: An argument where the intent is to have the truth of the premises guarantee the truth of the conclusion. Such arguments are valid when the intent is successful.

De Morgan's Laws (DeM): Rules that permit you to change and-statements into or-statements and vice-versa (e.g., ~(p∨q) may be replaced by ~p∧~q, and ~(p∧q) may be replaced by ~p∨~q).

disjunction: An or-statement (i.e., one with the form p∨q).

disjunctive normal form (DNF): A standard form for all statements in propositional logic. See Chapter 2, Section 5.

disjunctive syllogism (DS): A rule that permits you to conclude a statement, q, if you already possess statements of the form p∨q and ~p. More crudely, if it's either this or that and it isn't this, then it must be that.

distribution (Dist): Rules that work with or's and and's (e.g., p∨(q∧r) may be rewritten as (p∨q)∧(p∨r)). See the rules in Chapter 3, Section 3.

double negation (DN): A rule that permits you to drop two negations, when they apply to the same formula, or to introduce two not's in front of a formula (e.g., from p to ~~p).

effective procedure: One that can be implemented mechanically, and that never takes more than a finite number of steps. Proof-checking is an effective procedure.

equivalence: A statement of the form p↔q. See "biconditional."

equivalence (Equiv):   Rules that permit you to move among different forms that have the same truth table as p↔q. For example, you may replace p↔q with (p∧q)∨(~p∧~q).

exclusive disjunction: A disjunction that "says" either this is true or that is, but they both can't be true. For example, "Mary is now in Paris or she is now in Tokyo."

existential generalization (EG):   A rule that permits you to place the existential quantifier, (∃x), in front of an expression. See Chapter 4, Section 2 for an explanation.

existential instantiation (EI):   A rule that permits you to strip the existential quantifier, (∃x), from an expression. See Chapter 4, Section 2 for an explanation.

existential quantifier: The quantifier that tells you the claim is about at least one individual, x. It is written "(∃x)."

existential statement: One that begins with an existential quantifier.

exportation (Exp):   A rule that permits you to interchange (p∧q)→r and p→(q→r).

formal system: A game for playing with notation. One specifies the notation for the game, the well-formation rules, the initial strings, the rules for generating new strings, and the rules governing what counts as a legal result in the game.

free variable: One not covered by a quantifier. See "bound variable."

general predicate logic: A predicate logic (see below) that is designed to handle relations (i.e., to handle expressions that have multiple quantifiers and multiple subscripts).

higher-order logic: Logic in which quantifiers may range over sets and classes.

hypothetical syllogism (HS):   A rule that permits you to conclude p→r provided you already possess p→q and q→r.

identity, the principle of: The definition of equality (i.e., $(\forall x)(\forall y)((x=y)\leftrightarrow(\forall P)(Px\leftrightarrow Py))$. See Chapter 1, Section 6.

implication: A conditional statement, an "if, then" statement, a statement with the form p→q.

implication (Impl):   A rule that permits you to interchange p→q and ~p∨q.

inclusive disjunction: True when p or q or both are true.

indirect proof (IP):   A rule that permits you to conclude that a certain claim, p, is true provided you can derive a contradiction by assuming that p is false.

inductive argument: An argument where the premises do not guarantee the truth of the conclusion (i.e., probabilistic reasoning).

invalid argument: An argument where it is possible for each and every premise to be true while the conclusion is false.

law of the excluded middle: Every statement has exactly one truth value, and there are exactly two truth values: true and false.

logic: The search for good forms of argument, and the detection and rejection of bad forms.

logic gate: A piece of hardware the behavior of which mirrors the results of a truth table (e.g., an AND gate produces a certain kind of output only when it receives two inputs of that kind).

logical connective (logical operator): In this book, '~' for not, '∧' for and, '∨' for or, '→' for implies, and '↔' for equivalence.

logical form: An expression where placeholders for statements are connected by logical operators (e.g., p→q).

many-valued logic: Logic where there are more than two "truth values" (e.g., T,F,I (with I for indeterminate)).

mathematical induction: A two-step deductive rule of inference where one shows that the first thing in a sequence has a certain property and that for any n, if the nth thing has the property, then the n+1st thing has it. These steps permit one to conclude that everything in the sequence has the property.

modal logic: Logic that involves a qualification of the notion of truth (e.g., necessarily true, possibly true).

model theory: Analyzing and evaluating arguments in terms of truth tables or possible worlds.

modus ponens (MP): A rule that permits you to conclude q if you already possess p→q and p.

modus tollens (MT): A rule that permits you to conclude ~p if you already possess p→q and ~q.

monadic predicate logic: A predicate logic (see below) that does not handle relations (i.e., a logic without multiple subscripts, such as Bxyz, or multiple quantifiers, such as (∃x)(∃y)Lxy).

name (dummy): A term assigned to a unique individual, whose real (proper) name you don't happen to know. For example, let's call the first baby born in the U.S. in 1956 'z.'

name (proper): The term standardly assigned in labelling a particular individual (e.g., Cher).

natural deduction: A set of rules with which one can generate, at lower levels of logic, whatever can be proved without the aid of axioms.

negation: An expression of the form ~p, a statement that begins "whatever follows on this line is not true."

particular statement: See "existential statement."

predicate: A term designating a property.

predicate logic: Logic that treats relations among properties.

premise: A statement given at the beginning of an argument.

proof: A finite sequence of statements beginning with either given or assumed statements, each of which is produced by the generative rules of the system. The last statement in the sequence is that that is proved.

proof theory: Evaluating arguments by the use of generative rules.

property: A feature or characteristic of things, such as being red, or rectangular, or recalcitrant; something individuals can have in common.

proposition: The meaning of a declarative sentence, the entity that can be true or false. In this book, "proposition" and "statement" are used interchangeably.

propositional logic: Logic that treats simple statements, such as "The sun is hot," as unanalyzed elements and proceeds to examine the logical relations among complexes of these elements. See Chapter 1, Section 2.

quantifier: An expression that tells you how many things are being talked about. In this book, we dealt with only two quantifiers: $(\forall x)$ = For every individual x, and $(\exists x)$ = There exists at least one individual x.

quantifier negation (QN): A rule that permits you to switch to the opposite quantifier provided you negate before and after the quantifier and drop any resulting double negations.

recursive definition: A definition that specifies the simplest things having a certain property and then specifies the only means by which complexes may be constructed from these simples.

reflexive relation: $(\forall x)Rxx$ (e.g., everything equals itself).

scope of a quantifier: The portion of an expression covered by a quantifier, usually indicated by the left-hand parenthesis immediately to the right of the quantifier and the corresponding right-hand parenthesis. When there are no parentheses the quantifier covers only the predicate immediately to its right.

sentence: A string of notation satisfying certain grammatical rules.

simplification (Simp): A rule that permits you to conclude either p or q if you already possess p∧q.

singular statement: A statement about a named indivdual, such as "Fred is quick."

sound argument: A valid argument (see "valid deductive argument," below) the premises of which are actually true.

statement: See "proposition."

substitution instance: The result of replacing the placeholders in an expression with a particular case (e.g., replacing p with A∨B and q with

C∧D in p→q to get (A∨B)→(C∧D)).

symmetric relation: $(\forall x)(\forall y)(Rxy{\rightarrow}Ryx)$ (e.g., if x resembles y, then y resembles x).

tautology: A statement the truth table of which always calculates to true (i.e., a statement that is true in all possible worlds).

tautology (Taut): A rule that permits you to interchange either p∨p or p∧p with p.

theorem: The last line in a proof. See "proof."

transitive relation: $(\forall x)(\forall y)(\forall z)((Rxy{\wedge}Ryz){\rightarrow}Rxz)$ (e.g., if x is greater than y and y is greater than z, then x is greater than z).

truth: A feature of statements that obtains if things are as the statement claims they are.

truth functional logic: Logic in which the truth value of every expression can be determined by the truth values of its components.

truth table: A listing of the truth values for a given expression in every possible world.

truth value: In two-valued logic there are two truth values: true and false.

universal generalization (UG): The rule that lets you place the universal quantifier, $(\forall x)$, in front of an expression. There are restrictions on its use. See Chapter 4, Section 2.

universal instantiation (UI): The rule that strips away the universal quantifier. See Chapter 4, Section 2.

universal quantifier: The quantifier that tells you we're talking about each and every x.

universal statement: A statement preceded by a universal quantifier.

valid deductive argument: An argument where it is impossible for the conclusion to be false when the premises are true (i.e., an argument where if the premises are true, the conclusion must be true).

variable: a placeholder for a range of individuals.

well-formed formula (wff): Any formula satisfying a set of rules that specify what counts as a legal string of symbols.

Suggestions for Further Reading

The following list provides a sampling of texts with which you could pursue an interest in logic. The notation used in different texts varies. Thus, you might have to adjust by learning new symbols for "and," "implies," "not," and so on. Such adjustments are usually made very quickly.

Full Semester Introductions to Logic

Blumberg, Albert E. *Logic: A First Course.* New York: Alfred A. Knopf, 1976.

Copi, Irving. *Introduction to Logic,* Sixth Edition. New York: Macmillan, 1982.

Kahane, Howard. *Logic and Philosophy,* Fifth Edition. Belmont, CA: Wadsworth, 1985.

The Next Step Up

Copi, Irving. *Symbolic Logic,* Fifth Edition. New York, Macmillan, 1979.

Delong, Howard. *A Profile of Mathematical Logic.* Reading, MA: Addison-Wesley, 1970.

Jeffrey, Richard. *Formal Logic: Its Scope and Limits,* Second Edition. New York: McGraw-Hill, 1981.

Leblanc, Hughes and William A. Wisdom. *Deductive Logic.* Boston, MA: Allyn and Bacon, 1972.

Mates, Benson. *Elementary Logic,* Second Edition. New York: Oxford University Press, 1972.

An Excellent History of Logic

Kneale, W. and M. Kneale. *The Development of Logic.* Oxford: Clarendon Press, 1962.

Index

THE RULES

Conditional Rules		**Equivalence Rules**	
p→q p //q	Modus Ponens (MP)	(p∨q)↔(q∨p) (p∧q)↔(q∧p)	Commutation (Comm)
p→q ~q //~p	Modus Tollens (MT)	(p∨(q∨r))↔((p∨q)∨r) (p∧(q∧r))↔((p∧q)∧r)	Association (Assoc)
p→q q→r //p→r	Hypothetical Syllogism (HS)	(p∨(q∧r))↔((p∨q)∧(p∨r)) (p∧(q∨r))↔((p∧q)∨(p∧r))	Distribution (Dist)
		~(p∨q)↔(~p∧~q) ~(p∧q)↔(~p∨~q)	DeMorgan's Laws (DeM)
p∨q ~p //q	Disjunctive Syllogism (DS)	(p→q)↔(~p∨q)	Implication (Impl)
p q //p∧q	Conjunction (Conj)	(p↔q)↔((p→q)∧(q→p)) (p↔q)↔((p∧q)∨(~p∧~q))	Equivalence (Equiv)
		(p→q)↔(~q→~p)	Transposition

p∧q
//p
//q
	Simplification
	(Simp)
		((p∧q)→r)↔(p→(q→r))	Exportation
			(Exp)

p //p∨q	Addition	p↔(p∨p) p↔(p∧p)	Tautology (Taut)
p→q //p→(p∧q)	Absorption	p↔~~p	Double Negation (DN)